Australia • Brazil • Mexico • Singapore • United Kingdom • United States

NATIONAL GEOGRAPHIC

LEARNING

PAUL DUMMETT

Life

WORKBOOK | UPPER INTERMEDIATE

LEARNING

Life Upper Intermediate Workbook
2nd Edition
Paul Dummett

Vice President, Editorial Director:
John McHugh

Executive Editor: Sian Mavor

Publishing Consultant: Karen Spiller

Development Editor: Jess Rackham

Editorial Manager: Claire Merchant

Head of Strategic Marketing ELT:
Charlotte Ellis

Senior Content Project Manager:
Nick Ventullo

Manufacturing Manager:
Eyvett Davis

Senior IP Analyst: Ashley Maynard

Senior IP Project Manager: Michelle
McKenna

Cover: Lisa Trager

Text design: Vasiliki Christoforidou

Compositor: Lumina Datamatics

Audio: Prolingua Productions and Tom Dick
and Debbie Productions Ltd

For product information and technology assistance, contact us at
Cengage Learning Customer & Sales Support, cengage.com/contact
For permission to use material from this text or product,
submit all requests online at **cengage.com/permissions**
Further permissions questions can be emailed to
permissionrequest@cengage.com

ISBN: 978-1-337-28628-2

National Geographic Learning
Cheriton House, North Way,
Andover, Hampshire, SP10 5BE
United Kingdom

National Geographic Learning, a Cengage Learning Company, has a mission to bring the world to the classroom and the classroom to life. With our English language programs, students learn about their world by experiencing it. Through our partnerships with National Geographic and TED Talks, they develop the language and skills they need to be successful global citizens and leaders.

Locate your local office at **international.cengage.com/region**

Visit National Geographic Learning online at **NGL.Cengage.com/ELT**
Visit our corporate website at **www.cengage.com**

Credits
Although every effort has been made to contact copyright holders before publication, this has not always been possible. If notified, the publisher will undertake to rectify any errors or omissions at the earliest opportunity.

Text: p14 source: 'Interview: March of the Penguins', by Stefan Lovgren, National Geographic, June 24, 2005, http://news.nationalgeographic.com/; p40/p119 source: 'Your Baby's Brain Holds the Key to Solving Society's Problems', by Simon Worrall, National Geographic, September 9, 2015, http://news.nationalgeographic.com/; p46 source: 'Why volunteer?', Voluntary Service Overseas, http://www.vso.org.uk/volunteer/why-volunteer/; p78 source: 'Hayat Sindi, Science Entrepreneur', National Geographic, http://www.nationalgeographic.com/explorers/; p84/p126 source: 'Disappearing languages', National Geographic, http://travel.nationalgeographic.com/, https://livingtongues.wordpress.com/national-geographic-enduring-voices-project/; p102/129–30 source: Jodrell Bank Discovery Centre, http://www.jodrellbank.net/; p103/p130–31 source: 'RCP Insight: Taking a split medical elective' by Peter Ellis, Royal College of Physicians, http://www.rcplondon.ac.uk; p105/p107 source: 'How do I apply for a research grant?' by Thomas Egwang, February 13 2008, SciDev.Net, http://www.scidev.net/global/funding/practical-guide/how-do-i-apply-for-a-research-grant-.html; p108 source: 'Oldest Known Mattress Found; Slept Whole Family' by James Owen, National Geographic, December 10, 2011, http://news.nationalgeographic.com/, 'The World's Oldest Mattress' by Erin Wayman, December 14, 2011, http://www.smithsonianmag.com/science-nature/the-worlds-oldest-mattress-7513279/

Cover: © John Harrison/500px.

Photos: 4 © Jana Asenbrennerova; 6 © Julia Tsokur/Shutterstock.com; 7 © GlobalStock/iStockphoto; 8 Stephen Bures/Alamy Stock Photo; 9 Robert Fried/Alamy Stock Photo; 11 © Matej Hudovernik/Shutterstock.com; 12 © Lee Cohen/Getty Images; 14 © Frans Lanting/National Geographic Creative; 16 © Laura Stuzman/Sleeping Bear Press; 18 © Fitzer/iStockphoto; 19 (l) imageBROKER/Alamy Stock Photo; 19 (tr) AF archive/Alamy Stock Photo; 19 (br) © pikselstock/Shutterstock.com; 20 © dan_prat/iStockphoto; 22 © Catherine Karnow/National Geographic Creative; 24 © Renee Comet/National Geographic Creative; 28 (t) © 1000 Words/Shutterstock.com; 28 (b) © Natalia Bratslavsky/Shutterstock.com; 30 © Viktor Kovalenko/Shutterstock.com; 32 © Val Thoermer/Shutterstock.com; 33 © faberfoto-it/Shutterstock.com; 36 © James Nielsen/AFP/Getty Images; 38 Terry Donnelly/Alamy Stock Photo; 39 © AKauroraPhotos/iStockphoto; 40 © pavla/Shutterstock.com; 42 © fotoVoyager/iStockphoto; 44 Eye Candy Images/Alamy Stock Photo; 45 © PanosKarapanagiotis/iStockphoto; 46 © MShep2/iStockphoto; 48 © Ralph Lee Hopkins/National Geographic Creative; 49 © Radu Razvan/Shutterstock.com; 52 © rossario/iStockphoto; 55 © Steve Raymer/National Geographic Creative; 57 © mary delaney cooke/Corbis Historical/Getty Images; 58 © Vitaly Ilyasov/Shutterstock.com; 60 © Adriano Castelli/Shutterstock.com; 62 © Vixit/Shutterstock.com; 63 © Anan Kaewkhammul/Shutterstock.com; 64 (l) © woraput/iStockphoto; 64 (m) © lilly3/iStockphoto; 64 (r) © vesilvio/iStockphoto; 65 © Syda Productions/Shutterstock.com; 68 © Gordon Gahan/National Geographic Creative; 70 © Joyce Dale/National Geographic Creative; 72 © FloridaStock/Shutterstock.com; 73 © pierredesvarre/iStockphoto; 74 © Dmitry Kalinovsky/Shutterstock.com; 76 WDC Photos/Alamy Stock Photo; 78 Courtesy of Hayat Sindi; 80 © Pantheon/SuperStock; 83 © Jody MacDonald/National Geographic Creative; 83 © Marco Grob/National Geographic Creative; 84 © Chris Rainier; 86 FirePhoto/Alamy Stock Photo; 88 (tl) © Andraž Cerar/Shutterstock.com; 88 (tr, mbr) © Steve Byland/Shutterstock.com; 88 (mt) © L. S. Luecke/Shutterstock.com; 88 (mbl) © Robbie Taylor/Shutterstock.com; 88 (b) © Ulises Sepúlveda Déniz/Shutterstock.com; 92 © PeskyMonkey/iStockphoto; 94 North Wind Picture Archives/Alamy Stock Photo; 96 (l) maurice joseph/Alamy Stock Photo; 96 (r) © ERainbow/Shutterstock.com; 97 © Stefano Viola/Shutterstock.com; 98 © August_0802/Shutterstock.com; 99 © XPacifica/National Geographic Creative.

Illustrations: 25 Lumina Datamatics; 56 Kevin Hopgood/Kevin Hopgood Illustration.

Printed in China by RR Donnelley
Print Number: 01   Print Year: 2017

Contents

Unit 1 Relationships

1a A tradition in decline?

Reading friendships

1 Look at the photo. Then read the article. Which of the following statements best summarizes the difference in the French and American attitudes to friendships?

  a Most Americans have a lot of close friends.
  b Americans are friendly with everyone; the French only with a few people.
  c The French view friendship as something superficial.

2 Read the article again. Choose the correct option (a–c).

  1 Which of the following relationships does the author NOT mention?
    a colleagues
    b fellow travellers
    c fellow shoppers

  2 Psychologists believe that in modern society … have become weaker.
    a family relationships
    b friendships
    c all relationships

  3 According to the article, 25 per cent of Americans don't have … .
    a strong family bonds
    b a strong friendship
    c any friends at all

  4 Americans are known for being … people.
    a lonely
    b family-oriented
    c friendly

  5 French people are … about making friends.
    a careful   b worried   c relaxed

  6 The author thinks that in the West, we ignore the … of friendship.
    a significance   b qualities   c security

3 Find nouns in the article which come from these adjectives.

  1 true _____
  2 strong _____
  3 warm _____
  4 long _____
  5 deep _____

A tradition in decline?

Is intimate friendship a relationship that is dying out in modern society? In our busy lives, we have many acquaintances and friends – the people we work with, our neighbours, the people we chat to
5 at the local shop and so on. But how many really close friendships can we count? The truth for most of us is probably not many. Some psychologists say that while we still value strong family bonds, in recent times, friendships have lost the strength
10 and importance that they had in the past.

According to a study published recently in the USA, friendships in America have been declining in quality and quantity since at least 1985. The study claims that 25 per cent of Americans don't have anyone
15 dependable, that they could call a close friend. Yet, on the surface, Americans seem extremely outgoing and friendly people. If you have ever visited the USA, you will be familiar with the warmth and hospitality that they show to complete strangers. Everyone can
20 be treated as a 'buddy', even if they are just a casual acquaintance.

But in other cultures, acquaintances and friendships have different qualities. In France, for example, when you are trying to get to know a person, they may seem
25 rather cautious or even unfriendly, and the length of time it takes to form a strong friendship seems greater than in other countries. This is because for the French there is still a clear distinction between a casual acquaintance and a true friend. Although France is
30 changing and perhaps becoming more like America, there is no doubt that French people are still more private in their friendships and that they reserve real intimacy for their closest friends. This intimacy can be found in many non-Western cultures too, where
35 great importance is attached to the quality and depth of friendships. It is something that many of us in the West have forgotten and need to rediscover.

buddy (n) /ˈbʌdi/ a friend (colloquial)
die out (v) /ˌdaɪ ˈaʊt/ disappear
intimacy (n) /ˈɪntɪməsi/ closeness in a relationship

Grammar present tenses: simple, continuous and perfect

4 Look at the article. Find examples of the following.

1 two changing situations (present continuous)

_____
_____

2 three everyday activities (present simple)

_____
_____
_____
_____

3 two recent events with an impact on the present (present perfect simple)

_____
_____

4 one event that started in the past and continues to the present (present perfect continuous)

_____

5 Complete the questions from a survey on friendship. Use present tenses.

1 What person or people _____ (you / spend) most time with recently?

2 _____ (you / consider) this person or people to be close friends?

3 How many really close friends _____ (you / have)?

4 Do you think your friendship circle _____ (still / increase)?

5 _____ (you / make) any new friends in the past month?

6 How long _____ (you / know) your closest friend?

7 How often _____ (you / see) this person?

8 Generally, what qualities _____ (you / look for) in a friend?

Vocabulary friendships, describing character and phrasal verbs

6 Look at the article again. Find the adjectives that collocate with these words. You may use the adjectives more than once.

1 a(n) _____ , _____ , _____ friendship

2 a _____ bond

3 a _____ , _____ friend

4 a _____ stranger

5 a _____ acquaintance

7 Which word in each group does NOT collocate with the single word next to it? Cross out the word.

1 (a) mutual *friend / respect / student / interest*

2 a fellow *student / companion / scientist / traveller*

3 a close *acquaintance / relationship / friend / relative*

4 a *flat / faithful / travel* companion

5 a(n) *odd / happy / blood* couple

6 a(n) *close / old / passing* friend

8 Complete the sentences using the most appropriate adjective. There are two extra adjectives.

considerate   dependable   energetic   good fun
laid-back   outgoing   selfish   ~~serious~~   shy   unreliable

1 He seems very ___*serious*___ on the surface, but actually he's really _____ when you get to know him.

2 She's not stressed about arrangements for the wedding. She's very _____ about it all.

3 I do like him, but he's so _____ . He always forgets arrangements or cancels them at the last minute.

4 She's so _____ . I don't know how she manages to do a full-time job, look after three children and write books at the same time.

5 How could two people be so different? His brother is very _____ – he never says a word, but Simon is the opposite – very _____ and loves to be the centre of attention.

6 She's such a _____ person. She not only bought a thank you present for us, she got presents for all the children too.

9 Choose the correct option to complete the phrasal verbs.

1 I used to hang *out with / around* John a lot at college because we were both keen swimmers.

2 I'm meeting *with / up with* a group of colleagues on Friday. Would you like to join us?

3 I don't get *off / on* very well with my new boss. He's really difficult to work with.

4 Do you want to come *across / round* to my house and watch the football? It starts at 8 p.m.

5 It's very important to stand *by / with* your friends when they are in trouble.

6 Some people are very good at keeping *up with / on with* their old friends. However, I've lost touch with practically all the people I knew at college.

7 Lina and I were friends at school, but when we met recently, we just seemed to pick *off / up* from where we left off twenty years ago.

1b Young and old

Listening the ageing population

1 🎵 **1** Listen to an extract from a radio programme about the ageing population. Are the sentences true (T) or false (F)?

1 People are not having so many children as in the past.

2 People don't eat and exercise as healthily as in the past.

3 Older people are not as much at risk from deadly diseases as they were in the past.

4 The average age that anyone in the world can expect to live to is now around eighty.

5 People retire later than they used to in the past.

6 The ageing population has helped to bring families closer together.

2 🎵 **1** Look at the expressions from the radio programme, with their definitions. Try to complete the expressions. Then listen to the programme again and check your answers.

1 **the birth r_____** : the number of babies that are born per thousand of the population

2 **a baby b_____** : a sudden increase in the number of babies being born

3 **r_____ age**: the age at which a person stops working

4 **a (healthier) l_____** : a way of living

5 **life e_____** : how long on average people live

6 **the d_____ world**: countries which are economically and technologically advanced

Grammar past simple and present perfect

3 Complete the sentences with the correct form of the verbs. Use the past simple, present perfect simple or present perfect continuous.

1 There are a number of reasons. Firstly, the birth rate _____ (decline) over the last twenty years. The second reason is that sixty years ago, there _____ (be) a baby boom.

2 There's also no doubt that people's diets _____ (improve): generally we are more knowledgeable about what foods are healthy and unhealthy. So, people have a healthier lifestyle than they _____ (do) in the past.

3 Nowadays, people eat better and they _____ (also / learn) the right way to exercise and keep fit.

4 Lastly, we can't underestimate the enormous progress that medical science _____ (make) in improving the health of old people. We _____ (not / have) things like flu jabs or pacemakers fifty years ago.

5 These advances _____ (increase) life expectancy to around eighty in the developed world. Fifty years ago it _____ (be) closer to seventy.

6 Also people are working longer: in the last ten years, the retirement age _____ (rise) from around 62 to 67. Not only that, but they _____ (spend) more time looking after elderly parents.

4 Choose the best option to complete the sentences.

1 It's not just in Britain that people are retiring later. A lot of countries *raised / have raised* the retirement age. This *wasn't / hasn't been* very popular, as you can imagine.

2 In other countries, like France and Japan, the government *encouraged / has been encouraging* people to have more children. For example, in France, they *have reduced / have been reducing* people's tax if they have more than two children.

3 Some people say that advances in medicine *went / have gone* too far. They say that it *was / has been* better when people didn't live so long.

4 Old people seem younger now. My grandmother *had / has had* her seventieth birthday a few weeks ago, but she looks about sixty. She *has gone / has been going* to yoga classes lately too!

5 Emma *looked / has been looking* after her elderly parents for the last year. She *had / has had* to take a lot of time off work to be with them.

5 Complete the sentences with an appropriate time expression.

all morning	last year
before	since the age of sixteen
in the past	so far
just	yet

1 They moved to Canada _____ to live on a farm.

2 Where have you been _____ ? I need your help moving some furniture.

3 Have you had your lunch _____ ? I'm just going out to get a sandwich. Would you like to come?

4 Have we met _____ ? I'm sure I recognize your face.

5 I've been driving _____ .

6 Life was a lot simpler _____ , before we had a house and children.

7 I'm painting the house. I've painted three rooms _____ . Just two more rooms to go.

8 Zoe? She's not here right now. She's _____ gone out to get a coffee and some lunch.

6 Pronunciation auxiliary verbs *have* and *has*

a Read the conversations. Underline the auxiliary verbs *have* and *has* that you think are stressed. Circle the auxiliary verbs that are not stressed.

1 A: **Have** you finished using the computer yet? I need to check my emails.

B: Yes, I **have**. But the internet connection **has** been a bit funny.

A: What do you mean? **Have**n't you been able to connect or **has** it just been slow?

2 A: How **has** your visit to Scotland been? **Have** you had a good time?

B: Well, the weather **has** been terrible, but apart from that, it's been wonderful.

A No, it **has**n't been a very nice summer, but I'm afraid that's pretty typical.

b 🎵 **2** Listen and check your answers to Exercise 6a.

7 Dictation old and young

🎵 **3** Look at the photo. The person is describing her family. Listen and write what she says. What is she looking forward to when she is older?

1 I think my parents' generation _____

2 My parents _____ , but they both _____ . So now they can relax and enjoy themselves.

3 They've said _____ and that they don't _____

4 Considering that my husband and I _____

1c A dynamic society

Listening a study project in Vietnam

1 🎧 **4** Listen to an interview with a student who recently returned from a study trip to Vietnam. Which statement (a–c) best summarizes her views about the different generations in Vietnamese society?

a There is a deep cultural divide between the old and the young generations.

b All generations are confused by the changes taking place.

c The generations see things differently, but they all respect each other.

2 🎧 **4** Listen to the interview again. Are the sentences true (T) or false (F)?

1 Both the presenter and Lauren went on study trips as part of their university courses.

2 Vietnam is in a period of great economic and social change.

3 Lauren had the opportunity to meet a lot of ordinary Vietnamese citizens.

4 The older generation has suffered to reach where they are now.

5 Younger people are very aware of their country's struggles in the past.

6 Older Vietnamese people think it's very important to teach the young about the country's history.

7 Lauren felt that the different generations in the family couldn't understand each other.

8 The older generation is increasingly ignored by younger people.

3 Look at the phrases in bold from the interview. Choose the correct definition (a–c).

1 We were really lucky to get to experience that **first-hand** …
   a for ourselves
   b for the first time
   c something no one else has ever experienced

2 We **got to meet** …
   a had the opportunity to meet
   b were obliged to meet
   c met by chance

3 They **take** this new wealth **for granted** …
   a are suspicious of it
   b are grateful for it
   c assume it should be like this

4 They don't know **which way to turn** …
   a the rules
   b what to do
   c where to drive

5 The generation in the middle **bridges the gap** …
   a creates a space between two things
   b joins two sides
   c crosses from one side to another

6 The **30-somethings** …
   a the 1930s
   b a group of 30 objects
   c people in their 30s

4 Pronunciation word stress: *-ic* and *-tion/-sion*

a 🎧 **5** Listen to these words from the interview. Underline the stressed syllable in each word. What pronunciation rule can you make about words that end in *-ic* and *-tion*?

1	dynamic	4	generation
2	fantastic	5	restriction
3	economics	6	tradition

Rule: _____

b 🎧 **6** Practise saying these words, putting the stress on the correct syllable. Then listen and check.

specific	impression
italics	relation
terrific	interruption
scientific	transformation
characteristic	comprehension

1d What have you been up to?

Real life meeting people

1 Complete the sentences with the correct preposition. Some sentences do not need a preposition.

1 How's everything going _____ ?
2 I've been studying _____ my law exams.
3 You're looking _____ very well.
4 Being self-employed obviously suits _____ you.
5 Georgia was asking _____ you the other day.
6 Please give _____ her my best wishes.
7 How is your daughter getting _____ at university?
8 Say hello to her _____ me.
9 I'm _____ a bit of a hurry.
10 Good luck _____ the new job.

2 Grammar extra present perfect: simple and continuous

a Look at the verbs in bold in the sentences (1–4). Are they in the present perfect simple (PPS) or present perfect continuous (PPC) form?

1 He**'s moved** to New York for his job. _____
2 What **have you been doing** since I last saw you? _____
3 I **haven't seen** Hannah for ages. _____
4 She**'s been preparing** for her law exams. _____

b Look at the sentences in Exercise 2a again. Answer the questions.

1 Which tense emphasizes how someone has spent their time recently? _____
2 Which tense emphasizes a present result? _____

3 Read the conversation. Choose the correct options to complete the conversation.

Ben: Hi Sam. ᵃ _____ .
I've ¹ *wondered / been wondering* how you were.
Sam: Oh, hi Ben. ᵇ _____ .
I'm fine. I've ² *worked / been working* in Scotland for the last three months.
Ben: Well, ᶜ _____ .
You're looking very well. Have you ³ *decided / been deciding* to move up there?
Sam: No, it's just a temporary job. I've ⁴ *helped / been helping* to renovate an old castle. And ᵈ _____ ? Is Emily well?
Ben: Yes, thanks. She's just ⁵ *finished / been finishing* her nursing course.
Sam: Really? That's fantastic.
ᵉ _____ .
Ben: Well, ᶠ _____ .
I should probably go and do my shopping.
Sam: OK. Could I have your phone number again? I've ⁶ *lost / been losing* it.
Ben: Sure. It's 07945 699636.
Sam: Thanks. Well, speak soon, I hope.
ᵍ _____ .

4 🎧 **7** Listen to the conversation in Exercise 3. Complete the phrases (a–g).

5 Pronunciation word boundaries

a 🎧 **8** Listen to the expressions spoken at speed. Complete the expressions.

1 How _____ ?
2 _____ , thanks.
3 You _____ .
4 It _____ .
5 I _____ to work.
6 Sorry, _____ .

b Practise saying the expressions in Exercise 5a in the same way.

6 Listen and respond meeting people you know

🎧 **9** Listen to comments where someone meets a friend by chance in the street. Respond with your own words. Then compare your response with the model answer that follows.

1
Hi. What a nice surprise! How are you?

I'm fine, thanks. Good to see you.

1e News from home

Writing an informal email

1 Complete the email to a friend who is working abroad. Use the sentences and phrases (a–g).

a So keep your fingers crossed for me.
b All the best,
c How are you?
d Anyway, do send me your news when you **get** a moment to write.
e So, what's been happening here?
f I'm sorry I haven't written sooner.
g Dear Esther

---

1 _____

2 _____ I hope everything is going OK. 3 _____ I've been really busy at work the last few weeks. Everyone has been asking about you. How is your Arabic coming on? I imagine you're able to **get by** in most everyday situations by now.
4 _____ Well, shortly after you left, I **got** a letter from a fashion designer in New York. They saw some of my work in a catalogue for the shop that I work for and they want me to fly over to New York for an interview. I'm trying not to **get** too excited about it in case they don't offer me a job, but as you know, it's always been my dream to **get** a job with a top designer.
5 _____

The other big piece of news is that Eva is going to **get** married next year! I've met her boyfriend and he seems a really nice guy. They've fixed the date for 9th July. I hope you'll be back by then.
6 _____

It'd be great to hear how things are with you.
7 _____

Sophie

Word focus *get*

2 Look at the verb *get* in bold in the email in Exercise 1, either on its own or as part of a phrasal verb. Match the uses of *get* with a word with these similar meanings.

be become have manage obtain received

_____ _____
_____ _____
_____ _____

3 Look at the verb *get* in these sentences. Write a synonym for *get* in each sentence.

1 I'm sorry. I don't **get** what you're saying. Why do I have to wait? _____
2 Can you **get off** the phone? I'm trying to work. _____
3 I **got** this jacket for £20 in the sales. _____
4 Call me when you **get to** the station. _____
5 We had to **get** a taxi because there were no buses. _____
6 It was a bad cold. It took me two weeks to **get over** it. _____
7 They **got** first prize in the dancing competition. _____
8 Could you **get** the map from the car so that we can plan our route? _____

4 Rewrite this informal email.

1 First write the verbs in the correct tense.
2 Then see how many verbs you can replace with *get*.

Dear Martin,
I 1 _____ (receive) your email yesterday.
I 2 _____ (be) glad that you 3 _____ (arrive) there safely. It 4 _____ (sound) as if you 5 _____ (have) a really busy time.
Sorry to hear that you 6 _____ (be) delayed at the airport in the UK. I 7 _____ (hope) you 8 _____ (recover) now from the long journey to Chennai.
I hope the weather 9 _____ (not / become) any hotter too – 45 degrees Celsius 10 _____ (sound) quite enough! I 11 _____ (not / think) I 12 _____ (ever / experience) temperatures like that.
Nothing much 13 _____ (happen) here since you left. I 14 _____ (try) to find a new job, but I 15 _____ (not / be) able to find anything suitable yet. I'll let you know when I 16 _____ (find) one.
Louis 17 _____ (help) me to write a CV and a covering letter, because I 18 _____ (not / really / understand) the whole job application process.
Anyway, fingers crossed.
Good luck with everything there and write again soon.
Love,
Theresa

Wordbuilding forming adjectives

1 Complete the table. Form adjectives from these nouns and verbs.

~~ambition~~ adventure ~~care~~ child confidence ~~consider~~ control decision ~~depend~~ emotion ~~fool~~ fortune
help humour love passion patience ~~practice~~ ~~respect~~ ~~sense~~ self succeed support tradition

-ful	-ish	-ive	-ious/-ous	-ent/-ant	-al	-ing	-ate
respectful	*foolish*	*sensitive*	*ambitious*	*dependent*	*practical*	*caring*	*considerate*

2 Complete the interview about a family. Use adjectives from Exercise 1.

Are you a close family?
Yes, we are. We all have our own lives and careers so we are not ¹ _____ on each other, but we remain very close.

Why do you think that is?
We were brought up in a very loving and ² _____ environment. Our parents taught us to look after each other.

Is there a clear head of the family?
It's quite a ³ _____ family in many ways. On the face of it, my father is the head of the family, but actually my mother is really in charge. She's very calm and ⁴ _____ and never loses her temper.

And do you all share a particular family characteristic?
I'm afraid we're all quite ⁵ _____ people: we all want to be in charge and to manage everything.

Is there someone in the family you admire especially?
My uncle, who's an inventor. He's very ⁶ _____ with his hands. He can fix anything. He's also very ⁷ _____. He tells some really funny stories. I feel very ⁸ _____ to have someone like him in my life.

Has your family influenced your own path in life?
Yes. My father has been very ⁹ _____ in his business. He built it up from nothing. And I think that has made us all ¹⁰ _____ to succeed as well. My sister wants to be a film actor; my brother wants to be a top lawyer.

Learning skills extending your vocabulary

3 You can extend your vocabulary by making word families. Look at the word *decide*. How many words can you think of that are related to it? Complete the words and expressions.

- different parts of speech: *decision* (noun), *decisive* (adjective), ¹ _____ (adverb)
- collocations: *make a decision*, ² _____ *a decision*
- opposites: *indecision*, ³ _____
- synonyms: *make up your mind, come to a* ⁴ _____

4 Now write a word family for another word. Choose two from the list.

fortune   immigration   influence   obey
respect   support

Check!

5 Do the quiz. Choose the correct option. All the answers appear in Student's Book Unit 1.

1 Orang-utans are unusual in that they like to:
   a spend time with other animals.
   b share their food.
   c live independently.

2 Mutual respect is the respect that:
   a two people have for each other.
   b a person feels for their colleagues.
   c an old person gets from younger people.

3 In which sentence(s) is the action finished?
   a I've just read the new Elena Ferrante novel.
   b I've just been reading the new Elena Ferrante novel.
   c I read the new Elena Ferrante novel when it first came out.

4 The adjective from the noun *rebel* is:
   a rebelful.   b rebellient.   c rebellious.

5 An expression for saying things are always busy for you is:
   a busy like always.
   b busy as ever.
   c busy in everything.

2a True stories

Listening the Aron Ralston story

1 🔊 **10** Listen to adventurer Aron Ralston's story, which was made into the film, *127 Hours*. Which sentence summarizes what Ralston did?

a When he became trapped, Ralston panicked.
b When he became trapped, Ralston thought carefully about what to do next.
c When he became trapped, Ralston knew immediately what he had to do.

> **Glossary**
> **boulder** (n) /ˈbəʊldə(r)/ a large rock or stone
> **multi-tool** (n) /ˈmʌltituːl/ a tool like a Swiss army knife
> **numb** (adj) /nʌm/ unable to feel anything
> **wedged** (adj) /wedʒd/ caught between two surfaces

2 🔊 **10** Listen to the story again. Choose the best option (a–c) to complete the sentences.

1 Ralston went to Bluejohn Canyon:
   a to do some mountain biking.
   b to help prepare for a future mountain climb.
   c to do a bit of camping.
2 His hand became trapped when:
   a he stood on one of the boulders.
   b he dropped down onto a boulder.
   c he put his hand around a boulder.
3 The first thing he tried was:
   a calling for help.
   b freeing his hand with his multi-tool.
   c using his body to move the rock.
4 Ralston's options were to:
   a wait for help or free his hand.
   b wait for help or cut off his hand.
   c free his hand or cut off his hand.
5 After five days, Ralston finally:
   a walked out of the canyon.
   b was lifted out of the canyon by some tourists.
   c walked all the way out of the National Park.

3 Look at the verbs in bold. Match the verbs with the correct definition (a–c).

1 He **stretched** to reach a secure foothold.
   a extended his leg
   b stepped
   c bent his leg
2 The boulder **slid down** …
   a crashed
   b slipped
   c rolled
3 The boulder trapped his hand, **crushing** it completely.
   a causing it pain
   b destroying it with pressure
   c cutting it
4 He worked to **chip away** at the rock.
   a scratch
   b move
   c break little pieces off
5 **Dripping** blood, he made his way back.
   a letting large amounts escape
   b letting drops fall
   c trying to stop the flow

Grammar narrative past tenses

4 Complete the story using the correct narrative tense form of the verbs in brackets.

> On April 25, 2003, Aron Ralston [1] _____ (drive) to Moab, Utah, where he mountain-biked the famous Slickrock Trail. He then [2] _____ (make) his way to Horseshoe Canyon. When he [3] _____ (arrive), it [4] _____ (get) dark, so he made camp. He [5] _____ (climb) into the canyon on April 26. He [6] _____ (go) about five miles when he came to a section where a series of large boulders [7] _____ (hang), wedged between the walls of the canyon.
>
> As he [8] _____ (put) his hand around one boulder it [9] _____ (move) and [10] _____ (trap) his hand. Ralston [11] _____ (stand) on a small stone, facing the boulder that [12] _____ (crush) his hand. The problem was that he [13] _____ (not / tell) anyone where he was. It would be days before anyone realized that he was missing. By the time the search teams started out, Ralston [14] _____ (already / wait) there for five days. But by then he [15] _____ (decide) what he had to do.

5 Look at the sentences. If it got dark at 6.00 p.m., when did Ralston arrive in each case? Match the sentences (1–3) with the times (a–c).

1 Soon after he arrived at Horseshoe Canyon, night fell. ____

2 When he arrived at Horseshoe Canyon, night was falling. ____

3 When he arrived at Horseshoe Canyon, night had fallen. ____

   a about 6.00 p.m.   b 5.30 p.m.   c 7 p.m.

6 Choose the correct option to complete these sentences.

1 We stopped to rest because we *were cycling / had been cycling* all day.

2 After walking for an hour, I realized I *left / had left* my map at home.

3 We *started / were starting* out at 6 a.m. and didn't get back until 8 p.m.

4 The sun *was shining / had been shining* so brightly that it hurt my eyes.

5 We *checked / were checking* all our equipment before we started to climb.

6 I *cut / had cut* my knee when I fell over.

7 Pronunciation /æ/, /ʌ/ and /ɒ/

🎧 **11** Listen and underline the word you hear.

1	crashed	crushed
2	tap	top
3	stuck	stock
4	cat	cut
5	sung	song
6	drank	drunk

Vocabulary describing stories

8 Complete the description with these words.

background   drama   filmed   funny   key
moving   main   setting   theme   touching

Brooklyn is a romantic [1] ____ about Irish immigrants to the USA in the 1950s. The [2] ____ to the story is the hard life that people in Ireland lived at the time. The [3] ____ character is a young Irish girl who dreams of a better life. The [4] ____ moment comes when she moves to Brooklyn, New York, to work. This is the [5] ____ for most of the film, and where she falls in love. The [6] ____ of the film is family relationships. It is a slow-[7] ____ but very [8] ____ film: there are sad moments, but [9] ____ moments too. Also the scenes of Ireland and New York are beautifully [10] ____ .

9 Grammar extra present tenses for narratives

a Read this short review of the film *127 Hours*, the Aron Ralston story. What tenses are used to describe the plot of the film?

> **Film title**: *127 Hours*
>
> **Director**: Danny Boyle (*Slumdog Millionaire*)
>
> **Actors**: James Franco, Kate Mara, Amber Tamblyn
>
> **Genre**: Action film
>
> **Synopsis**: Aron Ralston, a 27-year-old hiker, is canyoneering in Utah's remote Bluejohn Canyon. An 800-pound boulder falls and traps his hand, making it impossible for him to move. He hasn't told anyone where he is going. Based on a true story.

> ▶ **GRAMMAR EXTRA narrative present tenses**
>
> We use present tenses to describe the plot of a book or a film and to review them.
> In the film 127 Hours Aron Ralston **is canyoneering** in Utah's remote Bluejohn Canyon.
> An 800-pound boulder **falls** and **traps** his hand.
> He **hasn't told** anyone where he is going.
> This use of the present tense is sometimes referred to as 'the present historic'.

b Look at the grammar box. Then complete the synopsis of a book using the verbs in the correct tense.

> **Book title**: *To the Ends of the Earth*
>
> **Author**: Ranulph Fiennes
>
> **Genre**: Autobiography; travel; adventure
>
> **Synopsis**: The mountaineer and explorer Ranulph Fiennes [1] ____ (give) a personal and gripping account of an expedition around the world from top to bottom. The adventures really [2] ____ (begin) once the group [3] ____ (reach) Antarctica and tensions [4] ____ (grow) between the friends, while all the time conditions [5] ____ (get) worse.

2b March of the Penguins

Reading a film documentary

1 Read the interview with a film director and answer the questions.

1 What is unusual about the lives of the penguins?

_____

_____

2 What is the theme of the film?

_____

_____

> **Glossary**
> **breed** (v) /briːd/ have children
> **chick** (n) /tʃɪk/ a baby bird
> **hatch** (v) /hætʃ/ be born from an egg

2 Read the interview again. Choose the correct option to complete the sentences.

1 The penguins make the long journey across Antarctica to _find food / have chicks_.

2 The mother penguins must make their way back from the ocean to feed _their young / the males_.

3 The director thinks the penguins' story was suited to film because it is _dramatic / romantic_.

4 It was easy to film the penguins because they are _friendly / predictable_.

5 The interviewer is surprised that the penguins can survive _out of water / in such hard conditions_.

Stefan Lovgren for

National Geographic News

March of the Penguins tells the remarkable story of emperor penguins who each year journey for hundreds of miles across the ice of Antarctica to reach their breeding ground. After laying a single egg, the females return to the ocean to hunt for fish, while the males are left behind to guard the eggs, which they balance on top of their feet. After two months of standing in the wind and snow without food, the males see the chicks begin to hatch out of the eggs. But if the mothers are late returning from the ocean, the chicks will not be fed and will die. French director Luc Jacquet spoke to us about the challenges of making _March of the Penguins_ and living in Antartica, where the film was made.

Your background is as a biologist. How did you become interested in penguins?
In 1992, I spent fourteen months at the French scientific centre in Antarctica doing research. I am a cameraman too and had worked on another film called _The Congress of the Penguins_. I was also inspired by the incredible beauty of Antarctica, and I felt this was a great story for the movies. It has all the elements of great drama – love, life, death.

In the film, the narration comes from the penguins' perspective – we hear their thoughts. Why did you choose this storytelling technique?
I wanted to get away from the traditional documentary style, where the action is described by a narrator. I wanted the viewer to feel like he or she was right there with the penguins.

How did you get so near to the penguins?
It wasn't difficult. They haven't really been approached by humans before, so they are not scared of them. Also they have very fixed habits. Their actions and movements can be easily predicted, so they're easy to work with.

How would you describe the overall theme of the movie?
It's really about the struggle between life and death. The penguins have learned to live where no other creature can. I was really impressed by that. How do they do that? How do they manage?

The penguins are bad walkers. How did nature allow them to make this terrible journey across the ice?
That's a good question, and I haven't found an answer for it. But I think if the penguins had the choice, they would prefer to spend all their lives in the water.

Grammar the passive

3 Underline examples of the following passive forms in the article on page 14.

1 Two verbs in the present simple passive
2 Three verbs in the past simple passive
3 One verb in the present perfect simple passive
4 One verb with a passive future form
5 One passive verb that contains a modal verb

4 Look at the passive forms from the article again. Answer the questions.

1 Which verbs have an agent after them?
2 What you think the (unmentioned) agent of the other verbs is (or could be)?

5 Rewrite these sentences using passive forms. Include the agent where necessary.

1 They released the original French version of *March of the Penguins* in 2005.

2 In 2006 the Academy of Motion Arts and Sciences gave it the award for best documentary.

3 You can see the film in over twenty different languages.

4 In the English version, they had changed the penguins' voices to the voice of a narrator.

5 Critics all over the world have praised the film for its interest and beauty.

6 Some people have also made comparisons between the lives of penguins and humans.

6 Read the last part of the interview. Rewrite the numbered sentences using the passive.

How can you bear spending more than a year in such a tough environment?
[1] People often ask me that question. I've met a lot of explorers in my life. Some spend their careers climbing mountains; others like to cross the desert or the sea. [2] Difficult situations have challenged all of them. It's like that for me with the polar environment. But once you have been there for a while, your body adapts to the cold. [3] The cold doesn't bother you so much. The wind probably causes you more difficulty – because it is so strong and it makes it difficult to move. [4] So you must keep your movement to a minimum. You mustn't run or hurry when you do a task.

1
2
3
4

7 Pronunciation weak forms in passive verbs

a Look at the sentences. Underline the verbs or auxiliary verbs that you think are weak forms (i.e. not stressed).

1 Where were you born?
2 I've been asked to give a talk to the whole class.
3 The book will be published next month.
4 I don't think we are being told the whole story.
5 Before the meat is cooked, the fat needs to be removed.
6 I was very surprised that you hadn't been invited.

b 12 Listen to the sentences in Exercise 7a. Then check your answers and repeat.

Vocabulary communication

8 Complete the sentences using the correct form of these verbs.

bring	engage	express	present	share
sum up	tell			

1 The best way to _____ your audience is to _____ a story that they can relate to.
2 A good documentary should just _____ information in an objective way.
3 It was a wonderful photo, because it _____ a very strong emotion.
4 Blogging is a very good way to _____ your ideas with others.
5 The film really _____ the story of the Apollo space mission to life.
6 I find that photos _____ my ideas better than words do.

9 Dictation describing a story

13 Listen to someone describing the book *A Week at the Airport*. Complete the sentences.

1 The _____ Alain de Botton's _____ , *A Week at the Airport*, is Heathrow airport.
2 The _____ that passes through the airport.
3 The _____ with travellers and airline staff.
4 _____ that if you are looking for somewhere that _____ , you don't need to look any further than an airport.

2c Children's stories

Listening the stories of Oscar Wilde

1 🔊 **14** Listen to a review of a collection of short stories by Oscar Wilde. Are the sentences true (T) or false (F)?

1 The stories were written for children.
2 The stories tell you something about human behaviour.
3 In the story of *The Happy Prince*, the statue of the prince can think, feel and speak.
4 The Happy Prince decides he wants to help the little bird.
5 The story of *The Happy Prince* has a happy ending.

> **Glossary**
> **foundry** (n) /ˈfaʊndrɪ/ a factory where metal is melted to be made into products
> **swallow** (n) /ˈswɒləʊ/ a kind of bird that migrates

2 🔊 **15** Complete the sentences. Then listen to the first part of the review again and check your answers.

1 The stories are suitable for _____ and _____ .
2 They contain elements that you would find in a traditional _____ .
3 At the heart of what makes them beautiful is their _____ .
4 People who read the stories are always _____ by them.
5 Oscar Wilde did not like to give _____ .

3 🔊 **16** Read the summary of the story of *The Happy Prince*. Then listen to the second part of the review again and choose the correct option to complete the summary.

The Happy Prince is [1] *a fine-looking / an old* statue in the centre of an old town in northern Europe. From his high position the prince [2] *feels superior to / watches closely* what is happening in the town. One day, a little swallow [3] *passes by / stops to rest on* the statue on its way to Egypt for the winter. The prince [4] *asks / orders* the swallow to take the gold and jewels from his statue to poor [5] *people / children* around the town. The swallow continues doing this for some [6] *days / weeks*. In the end, the swallow [7] *is exhausted / becomes ill* and dies at the foot of the statue. When the town councillors see the statue without its gold and jewels, they decide to [8] *destroy / repair* it.

Word focus *keep*

4 Look at the phrases with *keep* from the story of *The Happy Prince*. Choose the correct definition (a–b).

1 I still had to **keep back** the tears.
   a not let out   b dry
2 The swallow stays for some days **keeping** the prince **company**.
   a looking after   b spending time with

5 Complete the sentences using these phrases with *keep*. You will need to use the correct form of the verb.

keep an eye on	keep (someone) company
keep a/one's promise	keep a record
keep a secret	keep track of

1 Before they were elected, the government said they would make university education free, but they haven't _____ .
2 Those flowers are a thank you present from Sara. I _____ her flat while she was away.
3 My sister and I often visit my grandfather at the weekend, but during the week there is no one to _____ .
4 My friend is travelling around the world and she sends me regular updates so that I can _____ her progress.
5 Did you _____ of all your expenses? You know, taxis, meals, hotel bills and so on.
6 It's not fair to ask someone to _____ if they know telling it will help someone they know.

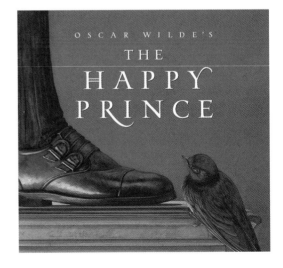

OSCAR WILDE'S
THE
HAPPY
PRINCE

2d What a nightmare!

Real life reacting to stories

1 Look at these situations where things have gone wrong. Complete the sentences using the correct form of the verb.

1 My trousers got caught on a nail and _____ (tear).

2 The key _____ (break) in the lock as I was turning it.

3 The boy put his head through the railings and it got _____ (stick).

4 He had _____ (make) a big hole in his jumper.

5 The pipe _____ (freeze) because it was so cold.

6 When it warmed up again, the pipe _____ (burst).

2 Underline the words or phrases that can begin each reaction. Sometimes more than one answer is possible. Then match the reactions to the situations in Exercise 1.

a *How / What a / That was* nightmare!

b *How / What a / That was* good thinking.

c *How / What a / That was* embarrassing.

d *How / What a / That was* lucky.

e *How / Poor / What* a stroke of luck.

f *How / Poor / What* strange.

g *How / Poor / What* you!

h *How / What a / That must have been* a relief.

i *How / What a / That must have been* awkward.

j *How / What a / That must have been* a disaster.

3 ☉ **17** Listen to two friends talking about a travel story. Answer the questions.

1 What was the problem?

_____

_____

2 How did they resolve the problem?

_____

_____

3 How did the speaker feel by the end of their ordeal?

_____

_____

_____

4 ☉ **17** Listen again. Complete the reactions (1–6).

1 Oh no. _____ you! What happened?

2 Oh, that's _____ . So did you leave her behind?

3 That was a stroke of _____ . And where were you?

4 How _____ ! Did they make it in time?

5 I can _____ . I hate being late when I'm travelling.

6 Did you? I don't blame you. I think I would have done the _____ thing.

5 Pronunciation linking and elision

a ☉ **18** Sounds in the following phrases are either linked (1–4) or elided (5–8: the last letter of one word is not pronounced). Listen and repeat.

1 large area   5 a burst pipe

2 immediate action   6 Great Britain

3 open air   7 hand baggage

4 cry out   8 bus shelter

b ☉ **19** Now say these expressions. Then listen and check.

1 thick undergrowth   5 pocket money

2 West Africa   6 credit card

3 dead end   7 nice shoes

4 climb up   8 first class

6 Listen and respond reacting to stories

☉ **20** Listen to five people telling you news. Respond with your own words. Then compare your response with the model answer that follows.

1

> *You'll never guess what happened to me yesterday on the bus. I started talking to this woman who I thought was Sue, my next-door neighbour, about my problems at work. But it wasn't Sue, it was a complete stranger!*

> *How embarrassing! When did you realize it wasn't Sue?*

2e A real-life drama

1 Writing skill using descriptive words

a Read this extract from a story and underline all the verbs and expressions that describe how people speak.

'Don't move,' she whispered, 'I think I can see an animal in the bushes.' 'I know,' Dominic replied anxiously. 'I can hear it too.' They stayed where they were, waiting to see what would appear from the bushes. Dominic, who was clearly very frightened, moaned quietly. 'Be quiet,' muttered Cat, 'or you'll attract its attention.' Just then, the branches parted and a tall man in white clothes stepped out into the clearing. 'Hello there!' he cried.

b Match the descriptive verbs (1–7) with the phrases (a–g).

1	he cried	a	she said unhappily
2	she moaned	b	she said complainingly
3	she whispered	c	he said loudly
4	he screamed	d	he shouted at the top of his voice
5	he muttered	e	he said under his breath
6	she said with a sigh	f	she said, not enunciating her words
7	she mumbled	g	she said softly

2 Writing skill extra punctuation

a Look at the sentences (1–4) and rules (a–d). Find examples of each rule in the sentences.

- Circle each example of rule a
- Underline examples of rule b.
- Double underline examples of rule c.
- Put a square box around examples of rule d.

1 He said, 'What a surprise!'
2 'I know,' she said, 'that you don't like eating spicy food.'
3 'Do you agree?' he asked.
4 'I don't agree,' he said.

a You must put quotation marks at the beginning and end of each direct quotation.
b Question marks and exclamation marks belonging to the quotation must be inside the quotation marks.
c You need a comma to separate the verb of speech from the direct quotation.
d If you break a sentence of a direct quotation and insert a verb of saying, you must put a comma after the verb and before the next set of quotation marks.

b Add punctuation to the following extract from a story with quotation marks and commas where necessary.

I don't think this is going to work Christopher sighed. We've been trying to build this canoe for three days and it still looks like a lump of wood. The wood's too hard he added. Actually, Christopher said Jen encouragingly we are making some progress. What we really need to do is find some better tools. Just then Tom screamed I've got it! Instead of using our penknives directly on the wood, why don't we make some better tools using our knives?

Writing a story

3 Write the opening paragraph of a story about two friends who have a scary moment while walking in the mountains. Follow these instructions:

- Begin with the most dramatic point in the narrative.
- Use descriptive verbs of speaking and moving.
- Use some direct speech. Make sure you punctuate it correctly.

Wordbuilding collocations

1 Choose the verb that you think collocates with each noun.

1 I've *done / made* a lot of **mistakes** in my life.

2 I'm getting a bit tired. Shall we *make / take* **a break**?

3 He *shared / split* **his ideas** with us about the future of the university.

4 I don't really remember what she said. I wasn't *paying / giving* **attention**.

5 Don't go out without a coat. You'll *catch / take* **a cold**.

6 I don't want to hurry you into the wrong decision. Please *have / take* **your time**.

7 The interview went well. I hope I *receive / get* **the job**.

8 She's very good at *saying / telling* **jokes**.

9 He's a very private person. He rarely *expresses / tells* **his feelings** in public.

10 Sorry, I have to go now. I need to *reach / catch* **the** 3 p.m. **train**.

11 No, I don't feel sorry for him. He *committed / conducted* **a crime** and now he must accept the punishment.

12 I try to *do / make* some **exercise** at least three times a week.

13 The teacher asked me to *tell / give* **my opinion**, but I felt embarrassed.

14 She wants to do a job that really *has / makes* **a difference**.

2 Look at these synonyms to do with speaking and movement. Choose the correct definition (a or b) for each.

1 We **trudged** for miles and miles in the baking heat. ....

2 We **stumbled** through the thick undergrowth, desperate to find a path. ....
   a walk while almost falling forward
   b walk wearily

3 He **muttered** something about it not being fair.
   ....

4 Try not to **mumble**. It's very difficult to hear what you're saying. ....
   a speak indistinctly because you don't want to be heard
   b speak indistinctly

5 She **moved cautiously** towards the door and turned the handle slowly. ....

6 She **walked back slowly** to the window and looked out. ....
   a go slowly
   b go slowly and carefully

Learning skills pronunciation

3 Without good pronunciation, people can't understand you. Read these tips to help improve your pronunciation.

1 Don't speak too fast. It's better to be slow and clear than fast and misunderstood.

2 Practise saying phrases and short sentences rather than individual sounds. Listen to native speech and try to imitate the sounds you hear.

3 Record yourself and compare your pronunciation with a native speaker's.

4 Listen to songs in English and imitate exactly what you hear.

5 Practise your pronunciation every day. Choose phrases and texts you have learned in the unit.

4 Look at these phrases from Unit 2. Follow steps 1–3 in Exercise 3 to practise pronouncing them.
   a What a nightmare!
   b That must have been a relief.
   c I can sympathize with that.

5 Write a mini presentation on a topic of interest to you. Read it aloud and record yourself. Analyse your pronunciation and note your mistakes.

Check!

6 Do the quiz. All the answers are in Student's Book Unit 2.

> **1** **What kind of film or book are these?**
>   a *Rush* ....
>   b *Cinderella* ....
>   c *The Hobbit* ....
>
>
> **2** **What were these people's jobs?**
>   a Peter Jackson ....
>   b Wilhelm Grimm ....
>   c Niki Lauda ....
>
> **3** **What are these three English idioms?**
>   a watch something carefully = ... an eye on
>   b what a terrible situation = What a .... !
>   c to suddenly catch fire = to burst into ....

3a No magic answer

Reading population growth

1 Read the text about the problem of overpopulation. Where does the writer think the solution will be found?
a in technology
b in population control
c in the sharing of resources

2 Read the text. Choose the correct options to complete the sentences.

1 The problem is not just how many people there are, it's how *rich / old* they are.

2 The economic optimists believe that resources *increase / decrease* as the population increases.

3 In the last sixty years, food production has increased *more / less* than the population.

4 Parents in under-developed countries need their children to *work / look after them* in their old age.

5 Bill Gates thinks that if we improve health in poor countries, the world population will not increase above *8.3 / 9.3* billion.

6 For Joel Cohen, *there are three ways / there is only one way* we can solve the problem of overpopulation.

No magic answer

For every problem we always hope there will be a magic answer that will make the problem go away. That's human nature. But problems like overpopulation are complex and demand complex solutions. First, let's outline a few basic facts.

Firstly, each person on the planet takes up space, consumes resources and creates waste. So the more people there are, the greater the problems of overcrowding, decreasing resources and pollution are going to be. Secondly, when people's standard of living rises, this has exactly the same effect. Rich people have bigger houses, buy more consumer goods and produce more waste. So even if the population remains the same, economic growth will create similar problems.

But economic optimists don't worry about an increasing population because, according to them, people don't reduce resources, they create them. For them, more people mean more human intelligence and more brains to find clever ways to boost resources. One example they give is the 'Green Revolution'. Over the last sixty years, agricultural food production has grown dramatically – faster than the population, in fact. Through the discovery of better seeds and plants, which are more resistant to disease, experts predict that there will be enough food for all of us in the future.

Another example is the Gates Foundation's work in fighting disease in poor countries through a programme of vaccination. You would think that saving lives through vaccination would actually increase the population, not decrease it. But parents in under-developed countries have traditionally had a lot of children to make sure that there will be someone to look after them when they are old. Research now shows that when you improve health in such communities, the population growth rate will fall within half a generation. Bill Gates believes that if we continue this work, the world population will peak at 8.3 billion by 2050 and then begin to go down. The current prediction for 2050 is 9.3 billion.

Of course, science alone is not the answer. It will help us to protect current resources and to add to these resources, but we will also need to look at how we share these. Joel Cohen, a professor at Rockefeller University, put it nicely. He said that three schools of thought had a part to play in lessening the negative effects of overpopulation:

• 'The bigger pie school', who say that science will increase resources.

• 'The fewer forks school', who say we need to reduce population growth and consumption.

• 'The better manners school', who say we should all share resources more equally.

The last, and probably the real answer, requires a different kind of faith: not in science, but in human nature.

Vocabulary verbs describing trends

3 Find verbs in the passage that describe things getting greater or smaller.

Greater	Smaller
1 r _____	6 d _____
2 b _____	7 f _____
3 g _____	8 g _____
4 i _____	9 l _____
5 p _____	10 r _____

4 Complete the sentences using an appropriate verb from Exercise 3. There is sometimes more than one possible answer.

1 The author thinks that one way or another, we need to _____ the amount of resources we use.

2 People expect the world's population to continue to _____ until around 2050.

3 After that, no one knows if the population will stay the same or start to _____ .

4 The economic optimists believe that even if there is overpopulation, we will find a scientific solution to _____ its impact.

5 One way to _____ the chance of having more children who will survive is to have more children in the first place.

6 Another way is to _____ the amount of money invested in health programmes in poor countries.

Grammar future forms

5 Read these comments about the views expressed in the article. Choose the correct options to complete the comments.

1 'Bill Gates wants to improve health conditions. He believes that as a result, people *will have / are having* fewer children. But what he doesn't say is that the result *will be / is about to be* more and more old people.'

2 'People who say they *will rely / are going to rely* on science to solve this problem are wrong. New technology creates as many problems as it solves.'

3 'I'll tell / I'm going to tell you something – I'll be / I'm going to be very surprised if the population growth rate *won't start / doesn't start* to fall in the next twenty years.'

4 'There are enough resources for everyone, but we *won't solve / aren't solving* the problem without sharing them more equally.'

5 'I'm suspicious of people like Bill Gates. He made a fortune out of business and now he says he *will / is going to* save the world.'

6 'Actually, *I'll go / I'm going* to hear Bill Gates speak at a climate change conference this week. It *will begin / begins* on Friday.'

6 Read the conversation about plans to attend a conference. Complete the sentences using the appropriate future form of the verbs.

Phil: Hi, Anna. [1] _____ (you / go) to the 'Future Foods Fair' next weekend?

Anna: Yes, I am. How [2] _____ (you / get) there?

Phil: I [3] _____ (probably / drive). What about you?

Anna: I haven't decided. Perhaps I [4] _____ (go) by train.

Phil: Don't do that – it's so expensive. I [5] _____ (give) you a lift.

Anna: That would be great. What time [6] _____ (you / leave)?

Phil: Well, the conference [7] _____ (start) at 10, so I thought about 8.30.

Anna: That sounds perfect. Do you imagine it [8] _____ (finish) by 6?

Phil: I hope so. I need to be back by 7.30.

7 Pronunciation /r/ and /t/ in American English

🎧 21 Listen to an American speaking about Bill Gates and other philanthropists. Complete the text.

There's a group of philanthropists in the US – Gates, Buffet, Rockefeller, [1] _____ – who have [2] _____ a [3] _____ of money to good causes over the last [4] _____ [5] _____ .

The problem for them is that, because they're so rich and [6] _____ , people get suspicious of their [7] _____ . So when they [8] _____ up, they often do so [9] _____ , like they did a few [10] _____ ago in Manhattan.

3b Smart technology

Listening homes of the future

1 🔊 **22** You are going to listen to an interview with a researcher about smart homes of the future. Tick (✓) the items you think you will hear. Then listen and check.

kitchen gadgets ☐   visual media ☐

water use ☐   security ☐

GPS systems ☐   lighting ☐

sound-proofing ☐   hot water systems ☐

2 🔊 **22** Listen to the interview again and choose the best option (a–c).

1 The aim of the radio programme is to find out which technology:
   a is going to be of practical use to us in the near future.
   b is the most imaginative.
   c will help us to be more environmentally-friendly.

2 Intelligent fridges will be more popular when:
   a they have been developed more.
   b they can tell you about the condition of your food.
   c they are less expensive.

3 Ultrasonic showers are not likely to be used soon because:
   a sonic waves do not clean the body particularly well.
   b we still have plenty of water.
   c they could be dangerous.

4 The researcher thinks that in the future we could sound-proof rooms using:
   a magnetic fields.
   b high-tech insulation materials.
   c energy fields.

5 Which of the following will we NOT do with a kitchen surface in the future?
   a watch TV
   b defrost a pizza
   c clean it by hand

6 In the future, we will be using electric lighting in our homes:
   a in place of natural light.
   b to reproduce natural light.
   c to help control our moods.

3 Look at the words and expressions from the interview. Match the words or expressions in bold (1–6) with the correct definition (a–f).

1 a new **gadget**
2 just a **gimmick**
3 water **shortage**
4 a **remote possibility**
5 sound-**proof**
6 **simulate** the sunrise

a not enough of
b a clever device
c something very improbable
d imitate or copy
e protected against
f a thing that just attracts attention, but is not useful

Grammar future continuous and future perfect simple

4 Choose the correct option to complete the sentences.

1 I'm sure we *will be hearing / will have heard* a lot more about this technology in the coming years.

2 In the future, cookers *will be making / will have made* our meals for us.

3 We *will all be using / will all have used* intelligent fridges when food packaging is intelligent too.

4 In ten years' time, the lack of water *will be becoming / will have become* a big issue, so we need to find alternatives.

5 In the future, people *will be using / will have used* energy fields that isolate a particular space from the rest of the house.

6 I don't think people *will be cleaning / will have cleaned* kitchen surfaces either in the future.

7 Soon, we *will be installing / will have installed* surfaces that can act as computer or TV screens in almost every room.

8 By 2025, smart technology *will be becoming / will have become* common in new-build houses.

9 Next year, our company *will be launching / will have launched* a new lighting system for bedrooms that simulates the sunrise.

5 Complete these predictions about the use of robots in the home of the future. Put the verbs into the future continuous or future perfect.

When people say that in the future robots ¹ _____ (do) all the boring chores around the home, most of us have an image of a human-shaped robot with a feather duster in its hand, which ² _____ (clean) the house while we sit with our feet up watching TV.

But if you move forward ten years, that is not actually the way technology ³ _____ (develop). In the future, robots in the home will take many forms. Vacuum cleaners that move around the room on their own are already available. In the future, we will see a lot of micro-robots, which ⁴ _____ (do) the kind of jobs that we tend not to do regularly. When we arrive home in the evening, micro robots ⁵ _____ (be) busy all day organizing items in our cupboards or cleaning our drains. These robots will already be an integral part of the equipment we use: the fridge, kitchen sink, cupboard, etc. We ⁶ _____ (not / acquire) them as separate items.

Vocabulary materials

6 Complete the sentences with the right material. The first letter is given for you.

1. I've packed all the books into c_____ boxes. But be careful, they're quite heavy.
2. The outside walls are made of b_____ , but the inside walls are wood and plaster.
3. C_____ is a much cooler material for bed sheets than nylon.
4. It's a nice belt, but I don't think it's made of real l_____ . I think it's plastic.
5. The new office building is a 30-storey structure of c_____ , metal and glass.
6. The soles of the shoes are made of r_____ which makes them light and comfortable.

7 Match the materials (1–8) with the most appropriate object (a–h).

1	a china	a	candle
2	a marble	b	frying pan
3	a silk	c	scarf
4	a silver	d	cup
5	a wax	e	floor
6	an aluminium	f	bracelet
7	woollen	g	gloves
8	a steel	h	pipe

Vocabulary information technology

8 Match the nouns to make collocations.

age   games   graphics   overload
programmer   security   storage   technology

1   information   _____

2   data   _____

3   computer   _____

9 Complete the sentences using one of the noun-noun collocations in Exercise 8.

1. The most serious issue of the next twenty years will be _____ : how we protect our personal and private information.
2. This post-industrial era that we now live in is called the _____ .
3. Augmented reality means projecting _____ onto our view of the real world.
4. Bigger _____ capacity means that portable devices can hold much more information than in the past.
5. People complain that we now have _____ . In other words, there is more information than we can absorb.

10 Dictation information overload

🔊 **23** Listen to three facts about the amount of information in the world. Write down the words you hear. Which fact surprised you most?

1   The weekday edition _____

2   Around a thousand _____

3   More information has _____

3c The simplest ideas are the best

Listening lifestraw

1 🔊 **24** Listen to a description of a device called Lifestraw and choose the best option (a–c).

1 Lifestraw protects against:
   a all stomach infections.
   b certain deadly diseases.
   c 90 per cent of all bacteria.

2 It is operated:
   a with a pump.
   b with a small motor.
   c by sucking.

3 In order to get the best out of it, users need:
   a no training.
   b a day's training.
   c a little advice.

4 It does not solve the problem of:
   a purifying salt water.
   b travelling to get water.
   c drinking dirty water.

2 🔊 **24** Listen again and complete the sentences. Use numbers and figures.

1 In _____ , the number of deaths from unclean water was _____ per day.
2 The filter traps _____ of water-borne bacteria.
3 Each straw costs approximately US $ _____ .
4 Each straw has a cleaning capacity of _____ litres of water.
5 The straw is _____ cm long.
6 Straws were used successfully in Haiti and Pakistan in _____ .

3 🔊 **24** Complete these facts about Lifestraw. Use the correct verb. Then listen and check.

1 Lifestraw _____ on a very simple principle.
2 It _____ protection against the killer diseases cholera and typhoid.
3 The filter _____ a substance called PuroTech Disinfecting Resin.
4 Each filter _____ up to a year.
5 It _____ very little, so it can be worn around the neck.
6 It doesn't _____ on electrical power.

4 Pronunciation dis-, dys- and di-

a 🔊 **25** Listen to these words. Is the underlined letter in each word pronounced /ɪ/ or /aɪ/?

		/ɪ/	/aɪ/
1	disaster	☐	☐
2	dysentery	☐	☐
3	diarrhoea	☐	☐
4	disease	☐	☐
5	diagram	☐	☐

b 🔊 **26** Practise saying these words. Then listen and check.

diabetes	discomfort	dysfunctional
distance	diamond	distribution
diary	dyslexic	disabled	diagonal

Vocabulary describing technology

5 Complete these sentences. The first letter is given for you.

1 Lifestraw offers a n_____ solution to a serious, complicated problem.
2 Because you don't need to learn how to use it, it's an excellent example of a _____ technology.
3 For many people in developing countries, collecting water is a very time-c_____ process.
4 Lifestraw's appeal is that it's a very h_____ gadget – portable, useful and easy to operate.
5 Although it is simple for the user, inside it uses c_____-edge technology to filter out bacteria.
6 WaterAid is worried that Lifestraw is a quick f_____ for a more complex problem.

3d I can't get the TV to work

Vocabulary adjectives describing problems

1 Match these adjectives with their definitions (a–h).

> blank   blocked   broken   cracked   faulty
> loose   squeaking   stuck

1 nothing will pass through it ....
2 not attached firmly ....
3 will not move ....
4 not working ....
5 has a break or split in it ....
6 making a high-pitched noise ....
7 with nothing on it ....
8 has a technical problem ....

2 Choose two adjectives from Exercise 1 to describe typical problems with each of these things.

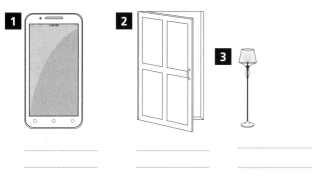

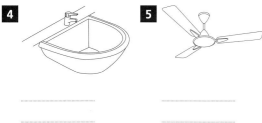

Real life dealing with problems

3 🔊 27 Listen to two conversations. Which of the items in Exercise 2 are they are speaking about, what is the problem with each item and what solution is offered? Complete the notes.

Conversation 1
Item: [1] ....
Problem: [2] ....
Suggested solution: [3] ....

Conversation 2
Item: [4] ....
Problem: [5] ....
Suggested solution: [6] ....

4 🔊 27 Listen to the conversations again. Replace the underlined words with the words you hear.

Conversation 1

1 Hello, I <u>don't know</u> if you can help me. I'm a bit worried about the fan in my room. It doesn't <u>seem</u> very safe.

2 What <u>is</u> the problem? Isn't it working?

3 Oh no, it's <u>going round</u> OK. But I think it <u>could</u> be loose …

4 Don't worry. They're <u>designed</u> to move around like that. It <u>shouldn't</u> come off.

Conversation 2

5 I can't <u>force</u> the TV in my room to work <u>whichever</u> button I press on the remote control.

6 Have you <u>thought about</u> switching the monitor on separately?

7 No, I didn't see that. I'll give that a <u>go</u>.

5 Pronunciation stress in two-syllable words

🔊 28 In two-syllable verbs, the stress usually falls on the second syllable. Listen and find the two words that do not fit this pattern.

> attach   compress   control   divide   highlight
> involve   open   prepare   reduce   select
> suggest

6 Listen and respond dealing with problems

🔊 29 Listen to someone asking for help with a problem. Respond with your own words. Then compare your response with the model answer that follows.
1

Can you help me?

Sure, if I can.

3e Technical help

1 Writing skill being polite

Rewrite the sentences so that they are more polite. Use the words in bold.

1   I want to pick up my bicycle on my way home from work tonight.   (**please**)

2   Can you help me? We need an engineer to come and look at our boiler.   (**wonder**)

3   Where can I find a battery charger for my old phone?   (**have any idea**)

4   I want you to send me an instruction manual for my washing machine.   (**could**)

5   I want to know how to download photos from my X306 camera onto the computer.   (**advise**)

6   What's the phone number for Apricot Computers? I can't find it anywhere.   (**know**)

7   I need you to show me how to use Powerpoint. It's for my presentation.   (**mind**)

8   What number should I call to get technical advice?   (**tell**)

Word focus *out of*

2   Complete the phrases with *out of* in these answers. Use the words below.

business	date	interest	luck
order	practice	print	way

a   Certainly. What day would suit you? Just out of _____, where did you hear about us?

b   I'd be happy to, but I'm a bit out of _____. I haven't used it for years.

c   That's because they went out of _____ years ago.

d   I'm afraid the manuals are out of _____, but you can probably find one online.

e   You'll be lucky. It's so out of _____ that probably no one sells them anymore.

f   I'm sorry. The technical advice line is out of _____ temporarily. If you give me your number, I'll get them to call you back.

g   Sure, if it's not out of your _____. Otherwise I can bring it in to work tomorrow.

h   I'm afraid you are out of _____ there. We don't deal with the X306 range.

3   Match the requests (1–8) in Exercise 1 with the responses (a–h) in Exercise 2.

Writing short email requests

4   Look at the situation and then write a short email to a friend asking for their help.

Situation
You have just bought a new hi-fi system for your apartment, but when you started to read the instructions, you realized you couldn't understand them.

Wordbuilding compound nouns

1 Match a noun from box A with a noun from box B. Then write the collocations.

A address   battery   credit   data
information   news   instruction   travel

B agent   book   card   life   manual
protection   story   technology

....

....

....

....

2 For each question, choose TWO nouns in list A that can form compound nouns with each noun in list B.

A	B
1 shop / estate / travel	agent
2 office / car / kitchen	chair
3 bottle / can / box	opener
4 bat / video / board	game
5 meeting / coffee / lunch	break
6 ironing / writing / message	board

3 Complete the sentences. Use compound nouns from Exercises 1 and 2.

1 I went to the .... yesterday to book my holiday. I had to pay a twenty per cent deposit with my ....

2 We have new computers at work with all the latest software, but I've no idea how any of it works. That's the trouble with .... It never comes with an .... telling you how to use it.

3 There was an interesting .... on the TV last night about a nine-year-old computer genius. He's created the world's best-selling ....

4 Is this your .... ? You left it by the cash till in the canteen during the ....

Learning skills personalizing new language

4 The best way to remember something is to make it relevant to you. Read the tips and answer the questions.

Grammar
Think about the grammar in this unit. Write sentences about:
a where you are going to go on holiday next year.
b what you are doing at the weekend.
c what your next career step is going to be.
d which person in your family will be the next to get married.
e what you will be doing in five years' time.
f what you hope you will have achieved in ten years' time.

Vocabulary
a Find four words from Unit 3 that relate to your life. What is their relevance?
b Think, in your own language, about your own predictions for future technology. Can you translate all the terms you used? If not, look up the missing words in a dictionary.

Pronunciation
Think about any words in this unit that you found difficult to pronounce.
a What were they?
b Do they remind you of any words in your own language?
c How do they sound different?

Writing
Think of something you really need some help with. Write a short email request in English to a friend asking for their help.

Check!

5 Complete the sentences. Then use the first letter of each answer to make an adjective which describes the world.

1 Another word for a clever device or tool is a .... (6)

2 Thomas Malthus said that people were 'basically .... '. (4)

3 The problem of too many people that was described in Unit 3a: .... (14)

4 Another way of saying 'before' a future date is '............................ the year 2050'. (2)

5 '............................ technology' provides the simplest and best solution to a problem. (11)

6 If you miss the opportunity to get something, you are 'out of .... '. (4)

Word: ....

Unit 4 Art and creativity

4a Art and creativity

Listening the graffiti debate

1 Look at the two photos of graffiti. Answer the questions.

1 Can you see any difference between them?

....

2 Which photo do you find more attractive?

....

Glossary
conviction (n) /kən'vɪkʃ(ə)n/ being found guilty of a crime by a court of law
outrageous (adj) /aʊt'reɪdʒəs/ very shocking and bad
vandalism (n) /'vændə,lɪz(ə)m/ destroying public or private property for no good reason

2 🔘 **30** Listen to a radio discussion programme about whether graffiti is vandalism or art. Choose the correct option to complete the sentences.

1 The event in the news that started this discussion was a graffiti artist *putting his art on the outside of a gallery / being put in jail*.

2 Handy thinks that the courts *must / shouldn't* decide what is art and what is vandalism.

3 Guy Francis says that *the property owner / the public* should decide what is vandalism and what is not.

3 🔘 **30** Listen again and choose the correct option (a–c) to complete the statements.

1 In the second half of the programme, they will be discussing:
   a graffiti.
   b help at work.
   c unemployment.

2 Guy Francis is an expert on the subject because:
   a he used to be a graffiti artist himself.
   b he used to be a journalist who wrote about the arts.
   c he works for the *Daily News*, a graffiti magazine.

3 Handy thinks that whether graffiti is art or vandalism should not be decided by:
   a the gallery owners.
   b the public.
   c the courts.

4 According to Guy Francis, Tox's work was vandalism because:
   a it was very basic and poor art.
   b he broke into the property like a criminal.
   c the property owners didn't want graffiti on their property.

5 Tox's graffiti consisted of:
   a writing his name and the date.
   b writing imaginative images.
   c drawing his name in many different colours.

6 The graffiti artist Banksy's work:
   a is very popular.
   b is very cheap.
   c has upset many property owners.

Grammar determiners

4 Look at the first sentence in each pair. Then complete the second sentence so that it has the same meaning as the first sentence. Use the words in brackets.

1 I have notified all the members of the club. (every).
I have notified _____ .

2 I think that both methods work. (either)
I think that _____ .

3 There were no celebrities at the opening night. (any)
There weren't _____ .

4 We've spent every bit of our money. (all)
We've spent _____ .

5 Each country has its own laws and rules. (all)
All _____ .

6 Everyone in the world is waiting to see what will happen. (whole)
The _____ .

5 🔊 **30** Complete the sentences from the radio discussion using these determiners. Then listen to the radio discussion again and check.

all	any	both	each	either	every
no (x2)	whole				

1 Is _____ case different or are there measures we can take that will help _____ unemployed people get back to work?

2 There's _____ difference in this case.

3 Graffiti is either art or vandalism. You can't have it _____ ways.

4 If Tox had put his work in a gallery, there wouldn't have been _____ trouble.

5 _____ owner of that property complained.

6 All Tox does is to write his name ... over and over again. There are _____ imaginative images at all.

7 The _____ debate of whether it's art or not is a different matter.

8 _____ type of graffiti could be considered art.

6 Choose the correct options to complete the short text about art.

There is [1] *no / any* way of telling what is art and what is not art any more. There is a story about a man who dropped his wallet in a modern art gallery. When he went back to get it, he found [2] *every / all the* visitors gathered around, admiring it.

The message of the story is that [3] *the whole / all the* modern art world is a trick and [4] *each / either* viewer needs to be told whether something is art or not before they can admire it. But were the people wrong to admire the wallet? If they thought it was art, some people argue, then it was art. [5] *Both / Either* views are possible. What's yours?

Vocabulary art

7 Complete the dictionary entries using these words. The words all contain the word *art*.

artist	artistic	artwork	arty	exhibition
fine	gallery	street		

1 _____ (n) an artistic creation, e.g. a painting, a sculpture

2 art _____ (n) a show or display of several pieces of art

3 _____ (n) a person who creates art (e.g. paintings) as a hobby or profession

4 art _____ (n) a place where art (e.g. paintings and sculptures) is shown to the public

5 _____ art (n) art which is found outside in an urban setting

6 _____ (adj) having natural creative skills

7 _____ art (n) the visual arts of drawing, painting and sculpture

8 _____ (adj) being very interested in the arts, often in a showy way

8 Dictation Banksy

🔊 **31** Listen to a description of the work of the graffiti artist Banksy. Write down the words you hear. Then put the sentences in the correct order.

1 The message was clear: _____

2 Often it carries _____

3 Despite not _____

4 Banksy, who is _____

5 Banksy loves to _____

4b What's on in London?

Vocabulary art and performance

1 Complete the sentences using these words.

> band   buskers   exhibition   gig
> gallery   halls   musical   performer   play
> show   venue

1 I went to a great _____ last night. It was a mixture of different acts. The best one was a circus _____ who did some amazing tricks on a high wire.

2 I went to a _____ at that new live music _____ on the High Street last night. I saw a local jazz _____ called 'Take Two Project'. They were excellent, I thought.

3 Have you seen the wildlife photography _____ at the Oxford Art _____? There are some amazing pictures in it.

4 Rodrigo and Gabriela are two Mexican musicians who started their careers as _____ on the streets of Dublin. They're now really famous and play in big concert _____ all over the world.

5 You know the _____ Macbeth by William Shakespeare. Well, the Victoria Drama Company have turned it into a _____, with singing and dancing.

What's on in London?

① The Alternative Village Fete

This fete at the National Theatre Square on the South Bank brings a modern urban feel to the traditional country village fete. Hosted by the organization Home, Live, Art, which has a reputation for producing art works in unusual environments, the programme includes live art, performance art which you can participate in with three National Theatre actors, communal country dancing, plus loads of food and other things to buy.

② Notting Hill Carnival

The Notting Hill Carnival is the UK's biggest street party. Featuring a parade of floats and a variety of styles of Caribbean music, dance and food, the carnival celebrates London's multicultural history. Join the party and dance all day and night! It takes place in the Notting Hill district of West London over the August bank holiday weekend.

③ Batman Live

Part theatre, part circus act and part visual and special effects spectacle, this show is produced by 'Warner Bros Consumer Products', which should, I suppose, tell you that it's not going to be a serious play. In fact, it's really just eye candy. Although the actors do their best, the storyline is not very strong. The emphasis is on the visual aspect, especially the set, which includes a fantastic giant Joker's head.

④ This is Design

The Design Museum has used various examples from its collection to make an exhibition which looks at the impact that modern design has on our daily lives. The collection includes classic designs like the Swiss army knife and the Mini car, as well as more mundane objects, such as road signs and work clothes. Most of the designs aren't new, but it's still a fascinating exhibition which challenges us to take a closer look at things around us that we usually take for granted.

⑤ The Floating Cinema

At first appearance, this event, organized by artists Nina Pope and Karen Guthrie as part of the Create11 summer festival, seems to be just a big screen on a boat. But there's more to it than that. Some films are projected onto the walls of buildings next to the canal where the boat is situated and one or two are followed by talks or workshops so that you can learn about the making of them in more detail. You don't have to be able to swim to attend, but you may get wet – the weather forecast for the weekend isn't great!

Reading out and about

2 Read the *What's on* guide on page 30 quickly. Find the following information.

1 Two events where you are a spectator rather than an active participant.

2 Two events which you can dance at.

3 Two events which you can eat at.

4 An event where you can work with actors.

5 An event where you can hear people speak about their work.

6 An event where different ethnic groups come together.

7 An event that children and adults can enjoy.

8 An event that you wouldn't normally find in a city.

3 Find words or expressions in the guide for these definitions.

1 shared or enjoyed by everyone (para 1)

2 a moving vehicle for performers, often decorated (para 2)

3 something good to look at, but without much usefulness (para 3)

4 everyday, ordinary (para 4)

5 don't always appreciate because we are so familiar with the thing (para 4)

6 seminar or discussion group led by an expert (para 5)

Grammar expressions of quantity

4 Choose the correct option to complete the sentences.

1 I really enjoyed the Alternative Village Fete – I even did *little / a little* dancing.

2 There aren't *much / enough* events like this in London.

3 There's *a lot of / much* international interest in the Notting Hill Carnival. *A large number of / A large amount of* the visitors this year were tourists.

4 I agree with the reviews – there were *plenty of / much* special effects in the *Batman Live* show, but there were *no / any* strong elements in the story.

5 We visited the website, but there was *a lack of / a little* clear information about the programme.

6 You don't see *several / many* new things at this exhibition, but you still learn a lot.

7 Book now, because when I phoned there were *hardly no / hardly any* tickets left.

8 There was *a bit of / a small number of* rain at the beginning, but it didn't spoil the show.

5 Complete the sentences with expressions of quantity. Use one word in each space.

1 There will be a small _____ of actors at the Alternative Village Fete.

2 There is _____ carnival in the UK as big as Notting Hill.

3 There were _____ amazing set pieces in the *Batman Live* show.

4 There are _____ of different classic designs on show at the Design Museum.

5 Hardly _____ objects at the 'This is Design' exhibition will be new for the viewer.

6 A _____ films are accompanied by talks and workshops to discuss them in detail.

6 Pronunciation weak form *of*

🔊 **32** Practise saying these sentences. Pay attention to the weak form of *of*. Then listen and check.

1 First of all, just a few words of thanks.

2 Most of the time, it's a bit of a laugh.

3 As a matter of fact, he's a friend of mine.

4 That's kind of you, but it seems like a lot of trouble.

5 Of course it was just a bit of fun.

6 In spite of that, there were a number of volunteers.

4c Music and me

Listening the importance of music

1 🔘 **33** Listen to four people talking about what music means to them. Write down the type of music each one is talking about.

1 _____
2 _____
3 _____
4 _____

2 🔘 **33** Read the sentences. Then listen again and match the speakers (1–4) with the correct sentences (a–f).

a Music is a way to escape from the boredom of your daily routine. _____
b Music can sum up what you are feeling. _____
c Music gives me a sense of belonging to a place. _____
d Music represents people's creative and independent side. _____
e Music is the most important part of our cultural identity. _____
f Music brings people together in celebration. _____

3 🔘 **33** Listen again and complete the statements.

Speaker 1

1 _____ music tells stories about _____ life.

Speaker 2

2 In Brazil we have a big range of musical _____ to draw on.

Speaker 3

3 Millions of _____ have been able to express their feelings ... by listening to _____ music.

Speaker 4

4 People figured out how to make new _____ using old _____ .

4 Match these verbs with the phrases from the interviews.

be connected to   (not) be important   discover
escape   seem true   think of

1 It's also **to do with** our history
_____

2 wanting to **break free** from the pressures of school _____

3 it **hit a chord** with us, for sure
_____

4 people **figured out** how to make new sounds
_____

5 they **came up with** something totally new
_____

6 it **doesn't count for anything**
_____

Word focus *spend*

5 Put the words in the right order to make sentences with *spend*.

1 he / a / clothes / month / spends / on / fortune / every
He _____ .
2 spent / trying / two / to / their / I / house / hours / find
I _____ .
3 there's / money / tomorrow / she / like / spends / no
She _____ .
4 together / haven't / time / much / we / recently / spent
We _____ .
5 spent / renovating / £20,000 / on / they / house / their
They _____ .
6 but / see / spend / don't / you / on / ages / manage / it / how
See how _____ , but _____ .
7 you / the / on / spend / night / us / why / Tuesday / with / don't
Why _____ ?
8 life / help / trying / has / people / whole / to / her / she / spent
She _____ .

Glossary
deprived (adj) /dɪˈpraɪvd/ poor
disassociate (v) /ˌdɪsəˈsəʊʃiˌeɪt/ break the attachment to
genre (n) /ˈʒɒnrə/ particular style or category

4d Personal tastes

Real life describing likes and dislikes

1 🎧 **34** Listen to a conversation in which Ian and Sue discuss a TV documentary. Answer the questions.

1 What was the documentary about?

2 Why did Ian like it particularly?

2 🎧 **34** Listen again. Does Sue like (✓) or dislike (✗) the following?

1 nature documentaries in general ☐

2 the *Tribe* series ☐

3 people who make programmes about others living in difficult conditions ☐

3 🎧 **34** Complete the phrases Ian and Sue use to express their likes and dislikes. Use up to four words in each space. Then listen again and check.

1 Oh, a nature documentary – not really my _____, actually.

2 I never _____ by them.

3 I'm _____ the presenter.

4 It _____ a bit actually.

5 I could _____ all day!

6 I guess I just get _____ people making these programmes.

4 Grammar extra word order with modifying adverbs

▶ **WORD ORDER WITH MODIFYING ADVERBS**

- Adverbs that qualify adjectives come before the adjective.
  I'm not **particularly** keen on reality TV shows.
- Adverbs of intensity come before the main verb.
  I **really** love musicals.
- Never separate the main verb from its direct object.
  I **like Bruce Parry** very much. (*I like very much …*)

Look at the grammar box. Then put the words in the correct order.

1 listen / all day / I / Bach / could / to

2 documentaries / anything / don't / for me / do / really

3 into / really / I'm / TV / not

4 particularly / on / keen / the presenter / not / I'm

5 I / get / reality TV shows / of / a bit / tired

6 TV / generally / watch / don't / much / I

5 Pronunciation disappearing sounds

a 🎧 **35** Listen to these words. Cross out the disappearing sound in each word.

1 documentary   5 separate
2 everywhere   6 restaurant
3 specifically   7 listener
4 interest   8 general

b 🎧 **35** Practise saying each word. Then listen again and check.

6 Listen and respond describing likes and dislikes

🎧 **36** Listen to the questions about your likes and dislikes. Respond with your own words. Then compare your response with the model answer that follows.

1
> What do you think of mobile phones with loud music ringtones?

> They really get on my nerves, especially when one starts ringing on the train or bus.

4e You've got to see this

1 Writing skill personalizing your writing

Complete the features of personal and impersonal writing using these words.

> active   avoid   contracted   formal
> furthermore   I, we and you   it   passive
> share   uncontracted

Personal tone		Impersonal tone	
a	Use pronouns (e.g. _____)	Use pronouns (e.g. _____)	
b	Use _____ verbs	Use _____ verbs	
c	Use _____ forms (e.g. *isn't*)	Use _____ forms (e.g. *is not*)	
d	Use phrasal verbs	Use _____ verbs	
e	Add personal details	_____ personal information	
f	Use conversational linking phrases (e.g. *what's more*)	Use formal linking phrases (e.g. _____)	
g	_____ your feelings	Be objective in your judgements	

Writing an online review

2 Read the beginning of an online review for a comedy show. Underline examples of the features of personal writing (a–g) from Exercise 1. Label the features.

> I've got to admit that I'm not a big fan of stand-up comedy. I always think that it's a rather unnatural thing. The comedian stands up in front of an audience who stare at him or her as if to say, 'Come on, then, make me laugh.' The comedian then has a few minutes to make them laugh or the audience will start to get restless. It's all a bit too aggressive for me. So when I went with an old school friend to see new British comedian Spencer Brown last Tuesday night at the Bristol Comedy Club, I wasn't really looking forward to it.

3 Read the next paragraph of the review, which contains some features of impersonal writing. Rewrite the underlined words and expressions using personal forms.

> [1] <u>However</u>, we quite enjoyed the show. And we [2] <u>were not</u> the only ones – [3] <u>his act seemed to be liked by</u> <u>the rest of the audience</u> too. Brown's technique is to [4] <u>commence</u> by telling a small joke – usually some amusing observation about daily life – which [5] <u>it is imagined at first</u> is the main joke. But [6] <u>subsequently</u> he builds on this by telling a joke [7] <u>that is</u> related to the first and then another. The effect of [8] <u>combining</u> jokes like this is that, even though each one may not be that funny by itself, the whole sequence is [9] <u>in reality</u> very funny.

1 _____   6 _____
2 _____   7 _____
3 _____   8 _____
4 _____   9 _____
5 _____

4 Complete the review by writing the last paragraph. Include a personal recommendation and details of when this show is on.

Wordbuilding word families

1 Look these words to do with the word *book*. Write the correct word or expression next to the definition.

> booking   bookish   bookkeeper   booklet
> bookmark   bookshop   book club   booking
> office   do things by the book   fully booked

1 a place where books are sold (n) ....

2 a group of people who get together to discuss a book they have read (n) ....

3 a reservation, e.g. at a hotel (n) ....

4 with all the spaces reserved or taken (adj) ....

5 liking to read and study a lot (adj) ....

6 a place where you can reserve tickets for a show (n) ....

7 a person who records financial information (n) ....

8 a piece of card which keeps your place in a book or a record of a particular website (n) ....

9 follow the rules or the correct procedure (v) ....

10 a book with only a few pages (n) ....

2 Complete the sentences. Use words and expressions from Exercise 1.

1 Sorry, tonight's show is .... We have a few seats available for Friday, though.

2 She's not an accountant, exactly. She works as a .... for Cole and Cole lawyers.

3 I've added their homepage to the list of .... on my computer.

4 This little .... gives you the phone numbers of all the council departments.

5 There's no need to make a .... The restaurant is never very busy on Tuesdays.

6 He's a very .... person, but not a very practical one.

Learning skills asking questions

3 You will sometimes need to ask your teacher or a native speaker questions about the language. Look at the questions (1–6) and the answers a student has given.

1 Is 'mate' a slang expression for 'friend'? *Yes.*

2 Do you pronounce the 'g' in 'recognition'? *Yes.*

3 Why do you say 'rush hour' when the traffic isn't moving? *Everyone's rushing to get home.*

4 Is there a similar saying to 'to make two hits with one stone' in English? *Yes, 'to kill two birds with one stone'.*

5 Is 'You're welcome' an American or a British expression? *American, but the British use it too.*

6 Does 'I wonder if you can help me' sound too polite or is it OK? *It depends on the situation: it is very polite.*

4 Look at these words and phrases from the unit. Answer the questions.

1 Is 'cool' a slang expression? ....

2 How do you pronounce 'comfortable'? ....

3 Why do you say 'either way' but 'both ways'? ....

4 Is there a similar expression to 'it hits me on the nerves' in English? ....

5 Is 'hip-hop' originally an American or a British expression? ....

6 Does 'I can't bear ... something' sound too direct? ....

Check!

5 Do the quiz. All the answers are in Student's Book Unit 4.

1 COMPLETE THE QUOTES.

a 'People are .... of surprises, aren't they?'

b 'Nature has done everything for Sydney, man nothing; man has done everything for .... , nature nothing.'

c 'There is no .... thing as 'bad' art.'

2 WHAT ARE THESE WORDS BEGINNING WITH 'F'?

a the countable equivalent of 'little' ....

b traditional, local music ....

c the adjective that describes art that is either drawn, painted or sculpted ....

3 WHAT ARE THE OPPOSITES OF THESE THINGS?

a a personal tone ....

b a little bit of luck ....

c spend almost nothing ....

4 REARRANGE THE LETTERS TO MAKE WORDS.

a music: igg .... , kubser ....

b art: largely .... , yart ....

c theatre: aply .... , lamicus ....

5a Urban development

Listening rebuilding New Orleans

1 📀 **37** Listen to a local journalist describing the rebuilding work in New Orleans after Hurricane Katrina. Are the sentences true (T) or false (F)?

1 A lot of rebuilding work has taken place in the French Quarter.
2 More than half the residents who left the city after the storm have returned.
3 One project is helping to build affordable homes.
4 The new homes are very simple, practical houses.

> **Glossary**
> **levee** (n) /ˈlevi/ a barrier to protect an area from flooding
> **spare** (v) /speə/ save from something
> **tidal wave** (n) /ˈtaɪd(ə)l weɪv/ a very large wave (that can destroy things and cause damage when it hits the land)

2 📀 **37** Listen to the journalist again and complete the sentences.

1 For most tourists who visit the French Quarter in New Orleans these days, things seem to be ....
2 Most of the damage in New Orleans was caused by the .... , not the ....
3 After the storm, a few New Orleanians decided to .... in other places.
4 The redevelopment plan for New Orleans has not been systematic or ....
5 The Lower 9th Ward was a pretty .... area of New Orleans, even before the storm.
6 The new homes are .... and environmentally-friendly.
7 The journalist thought the architecture of the buildings was very ....
8 Some critics say that the houses are not ....

Grammar verb + infinitive or *-ing*

3 Look at the sentences from the report about the rebuilding work in New Orleans. Choose the correct option to complete the sentences.

1 In the French Quarter, everything now seems *being / to be* back to normal.
2 In other areas, you keep on *seeing / to see* the effects of the disaster.
3 The city's levees failed *holding / to hold* back the big tidal wave.
4 About two-thirds of the residents have managed *returning / to return* to the city.
5 A few people decided *resettling / to resettle* elsewhere.
6 One project proposed *building / to build* 150 affordable homes.
7 No one wants to risk *seeing / to see* their home flood again.
8 You can't help *wondering / to wonder* how many more homes could have been built.

4 Complete the table with these verbs. Some verbs can go in more than one category.

allow	ask	carry on	enjoy	get
help	hope	imagine	make	want

verb + *to* + infinitive	verb + *someone* + *to* + infinitive

verb + *-ing*	verb + *someone* + infinitive

5 Grammar extra verb + infinitive or *-ing*

a Put these verbs into the correct column in the table in Exercise 4 on page 36.

avoid	choose	finish	force	involve
learn	let	(not) mind	teach	

b Complete the text about volunteering in New Orleans. Use the correct form of the verb in brackets.

If you want [1] .... (visit) New Orleans as a tourist, but would also like to do something to help local people [2] .... (rebuild) their lives while you are there, you could work as a volunteer on a project. There are lots of organizations that allow visitors [3] .... (participate) for a week or even a few days. If you don't mind [4] .... (do) physical work, you could do some labouring on a building project. Alternatively, you could choose [5] .... (work) with children or help out at a local museum. Some of the projects might involve [6] .... (learn) a few new skills, but no one will force you [7] .... (do) something you feel uncomfortable with. And don't worry about not having fun. You will have plenty of time off and you'll also enjoy [8] .... (meet) New Orleanians – something a regular tourist might find more difficult.

Vocabulary urban features

6 Complete the announcement by a city's planning committee. Use these words.

blocks	centre (x2)	luxury	park
pedestrian	residential	spaces	

On 2nd July, the City Council's Planning committee met and agreed the following actions to **redevelop** the city centre:

• The centre should become a [1] .... zone to allow shoppers and visitors to walk around more freely.
• The old shopping [2] .... in Prince's Street, next to the river, will be replaced by a new [3] .... area made up of some low-cost homes and some [4] .... apartments. The council

promises there will be plenty of green [5] .... in the new development.
• The Council also plans to **knock down** two large office [6] .... in the centre, which they think **spoil** its appearance. They want to encourage companies to move to a new business [7] .... north of the city.
• The council also proposes to **modernize** the leisure [8] .... and **turn** the existing car park **into** a play area for children.

7 Match the verbs in bold in the announcement in Exercise 6 with these verbs.

1 destroy ....
2 convert into ....
3 damage ....
4 bring up to date ....
5 rebuild ....

8 Dictation a New Orleanian speaks

a 🔊 **38** Listen to a New Orleans resident describing life since Hurricane Katrina. Write down the words you hear. Is the resident happy living in New Orleans?

The fact that ....

....

....

....

....

I'm a musician ....

....

....

....

But since Hurricane Katrina, ...

....

....

....

....

b Underline examples of verb + infinitive or verb + *-ing* in your answer in Exercise 8a.

5b Monterey Bay

Reading changing places

1 Read the article about Monterey Bay. Which of the following sentences are true of Monterey today?

  a   It has an important tourist industry.
  b   It is a very culturally diverse place.
  c   It has an important fishing industry.
  d   There is little sea-life left.

2 Read the article again. Are the sentences true (T) or false (F)? Or is there not enough information (N) to say if the statements are true or false?

  1   In the last 150 years, Monterey's main industry has been tourism, then fishing, then tourism again.
  2   Canning was a process that was invented in Monterey.
  3   Carl Danielsen was born in Norway.
  4   A lot of immigrants came to Monterey to take advantage of the boom in fishing.
  5   The reason for the disappearance of the sardines is unclear.
  6   Otters eat abalone.
  7   It's impossible to make a living from fishing in Monterey these days.
  8   The old character of Monterey still remains.

3 Find words or phrases in the passage with the following definitions.

  1   constantly changing (para 1)

  2   be part of the good times (para 2)

  3   suddenly (para 3)

  4   senior and experienced people (para 3)

  5   establish, start (para 3)

  6   try out (para 4)

Glossary
abalone (n) /ˌæbəˈləʊni/ a small edible shellfish
canning process (n) /ˈkænɪŋ ˈprəʊses/ preserving food by putting it in a tin
otter (n) /ˈɒtə(r)/ a small river or sea animal
sardine (n) /sɑː(r)ˈdiːn/ a small, edible silver fish

Monterey Bay

The history and development of Monterey Bay is a dynamic one. 150 years ago, tourism was its main industry, as it is again today. But a lot of changes have taken place in that period. Carl Danielsen, a fisherman in Monterey for the last 60 years, describes these changes.

'My father was a fisherman and his father before him. I first started going out to sea with my daddy when I was seven years old. In those days, there were a lot of sardines in the sea and Monterey took advantage of the newly-developed canning process, which meant that enormous amounts of fish could be preserved in a way that wasn't possible before. In the 1930s, Monterey was the world capital of the sardine canning industry and fishing was big business here. That was when my parents came over from Norway, along with other immigrants from Japan, China, Italy – you name it. Everyone wanted to join in the party. That's one of the reasons that Monterey is such a cosmopolitan place now.

Then in the 1950s, the sardines disappeared – just like that. No one knows why. Some people say it was because of overfishing; others say it was just part of the natural ocean cycle. One thing is for sure, and that is that fishing isn't the simple industry it was in the 1950s – I wish it was. There have been so many rules and regulations since then, controlling what and where you can fish. You can't collect abalone, for example, anymore – unless you're an otter, that is! Old-timers like me continue to fish, but it's not an easy life and many people have set up other businesses. Most are tourist-related, like boat trips, sightseeing trips and fishing trips, but all of them are connected with the sea and sea-life. We have a fantastic range of sea-life here: otters, whales, dolphins, and so on.

So today, tourism is the main industry here, but the essential character of the bay hasn't changed. The old canning factory has become an aquarium and a research centre for sea-life. There are lots of restaurants along the sea front, which do great business. I'd recommend any visitor to Monterey to sample the seafood. It's fantastic.'

4 Complete the sentences with the correct adjective. Use the nouns in brackets to help you.

1 Monterey is a _____ place. (dynamism)
2 In the 1930s, Monterey was a more _____ city. (industry)
3 Now it has become an _____ destination for tourists. (attraction)
4 The old harbour is well _____. (preservation)
5 These days, fishing is strongly _____. (regulation)
6 But the _____ character of the bay hasn't changed. (essence)

Grammar verbs with both *-ing* and *to* + infinitive

5 Read the pairs of sentences. Do the verbs have a change in their meaning (C) or no change in meaning (NC)?

1 a When did they **start** to can sardines in Monterey?
  b When did they **start** canning sardines in Monterey? _____

2 a People **continued** to can sardines in Monterey until the 1980s.
  b People **continued** canning sardines in Monterey until the 1980s. _____

3 a I **stopped** to visit my aunt in California last year.
  b I **stopped** visiting my aunt in California last year. _____

4 a Did you **remember** to bring a guidebook?
  b Did you **remember** bringing a guidebook? _____

5 a I **like** to watch sea-life in the wild.
  b I **like** watching sea-life in the wild. _____

6 a I **prefer** to eat fresh fish to frozen.
  b I **prefer** eating fresh fish to frozen. _____

7 a He **went on** to work as a fisherman.
  b He **went on** working as a fisherman. _____

8 a Every fisherman **means** to get up early in the morning.
  b Being a fisherman **means** getting up early each morning. _____

6 Complete the sentences using the *-ing* form or *to* + infinitive.

1 Carl remembers _____ (go) fishing with his father in the 1950s.
2 In those days, preserving fish meant _____ (put) them into cans.
3 In the 1950s, fishermen had to stop _____ (catch) sardines.
4 Carl regrets _____ (say) that fishing is not a simple industry anymore.
5 Some older fishermen have gone on _____ (fish) to this day.
6 They try _____ (make) a living from it, but it's not an easy way of life.
7 Other fishermen stopped fishing _____ (go) into the tourist business.
8 Visitors to Monterey should try _____ (eat) the fresh seafood.

7 Choose the correct option to complete the text.

A lot of people visit Monterey Bay before going on [1] *visiting / to visit* San Francisco and Yosemite National Park in California. One thing they stop [2] *seeing / to see* are the otters which live in the harbour. While eating your lunch at a waterfront restaurant, you can watch them playing in the water or trying [3] *opening / to open* shellfish by breaking them against the fishing boats. Although the otters don't mean [4] *doing / to do* any harm, it annoys the fishermen because it means [5] *having / to have* to paint their boats more often!

8 Pronunciation rhyming words

🔊 **39** Make pairs of rhyming words. Match the words in box A with the word that rhymes from box B. Then listen and check.

A				
China	found	front	meant	ocean
placed	rule	way	whale	where

B				
drowned	hunt	minor	motion	sent
share	taste	they'll	tool	weigh

5c Language development

Listening 30 million words

1 💿 **40** Read the summary about a new book about language and children. Then listen to a radio news report. Choose the correct options to complete the summary.

If young children are exposed to rich language, it helps them [1] *now / in later life* because it helps them to learn other [2] *things / languages*. The author of the book, Dana Suskind, says that we should [3] *talk / play* with our children more and forget about them learning with [4] *books / technology*. The title of the book is a reference to the fact that poor children hear 30 million fewer words than better off children in the first [5] *three / six* years of their lives.

> **Glossary**
> **dominate** (v) /ˈdɒmɪneɪt/ be the controlling force over something
> **exposure** (to) (n) /ɪkˈspəʊʒə(r) tʊ/ giving someone experience of something
> **nappy** (n) /naepɪ/ pants babies wear before they are trained to use the toilet

2 💿 **40** Listen to the news report again. Answer the question.

1 What things does exposure to rich language help a child with?

2 What are the four T's?
Tune i_____, Talk more, Take turns and Turn o_____ the technology.

3 What does 'take turns' mean in the report?

4 What do most adults not realize about babies?

5 What cannot show empathy (understanding what another person is feeling)?

6 How many more words have children from richer backgrounds heard by the time they are three years old?

3 Look at the audioscript on page 119. Find words or phrases with the following meanings.

1 very important (para 1) _____

2 understanding the relation between you and objects around you (para 2) _____

3 a spoken account of what is happening (para 3) _____

4 a signal that you make with your face (para 3) _____

5 communicating with others (para 4) _____

6 a fact in the form of a number (para 5) _____

Word focus *fall*

4 Complete the expressions. Use the word *fall* with the correct prepositions.

1 It's very important to try to keep to your work schedule. Because if you **fall** _____, you'll find it very difficult to catch up again.

2 I didn't believe in love at first sight until I met Harry. I **fell** _____ him immediately.

3 We were supposed to visit my parents at the weekend, but our plans **fell** _____ because my mother rang and said she had the flu.

4 We really need some new curtains. Those ones look terrible and they're beginning to **fall** _____.

5 I used to run the business with a friend but I **fell** _____ with her over our future plans.

6 The flowers were on a table just behind the door, so when I opened the door, the vase of flowers **fell** _____.

5 Pronunciation antepenultimate stress

a 💿 **41** Often in words of three or more syllables, the stress falls on the third syllable from the end. Listen to the stress in these words and repeat.

photo<u>graph</u>   pho<u>to</u>grapher
<u>ana</u>lyse   a<u>na</u>lysis   ana<u>ly</u>tical

b 💿 **42** Underline the stressed syllable in these words. Then listen, check and repeat.

commentary   ability
dominate   development
empathy   technology
influence
powerful

5d A controversial issue

Real life debating issues

1 Match phrases (1–7) from list A with phrases with a similar meaning (a–g) from list B.

A	B
1 I'm not too bothered by …	a Yes, absolutely.
2 I think that …	b Not necessarily.
3 I think we're forgetting that …	c The point is that …
	d I'm less concerned about …
4 I agree completely.	e For me, …
5 The thing is that …	f Sorry, but I don't think that's right.
6 No, I don't accept that.	g We need to remember that …
7 Well, that depends.	

2 Look at these phrases about urban features. Write the opposites.

1 private transport
p_____ transport

2 out-of-town shops
l_____ shops

3 built-up areas
g_____ spaces

4 streets where cars can drive
p_____ zones

5 places where people work
l_____ facilities

3 🎧 **43** Listen to two conversations about urban development. What is the subject (a–e) of each conversation?

Conversation 1: _____

Conversation 2: _____

a a lack of affordable housing
b a lack of leisure facilities
c a lack of public transport
d redevelopment of shops in the city centre
e traffic in the city centre

4 🎧 **43** Listen to the conversations again. Choose the expressions that you hear.

Conversation 1
A: Do you know, ¹ *it seems / I find it* incredible that in a big city like this there aren't more leisure facilities and green spaces. We've got one ancient swimming pool, a couple of tennis courts and a few children's playgrounds.
B: I know and ² *I think so too / I agree completely.* I think we should try and get a letter signed by as many people as possible asking the council to do something about it.
A: ³ *The thing is / The fact is* it's our taxes they're spending.
B: Yes, ⁴ *absolutely / I agree*, so we really ought to have a say in how the money is spent, and I think leisure facilities should be a priority.

Conversation 2
B: Have you seen the plans to reduce traffic in the centre of town? They look awful. I think they should just make the whole centre a pedestrian area. ⁵ *For me, / I think* that would ⁶ *be much better / make much more sense.*
A: Well, I ⁷ *understand / appreciate* why you say that and I used to think the same. But actually, ⁸ *you also need to consider / you're forgetting about* all the old people who depend on buses and public transport. ⁹ *The real issue is / I'm more concerned* that they just wouldn't be able to come into the town centre and use local shops anymore if vehicles were banned.
B: ¹⁰ *That depends. / Not necessarily.* It seems to work in other city centres.

5 Pronunciation sentence stress

a Look at these sentences. Which words are most stressed in each phrase?

1 I know and I agree completely.

2 The thing is, it's our taxes they're spending.

3 For me, that would make much more sense.

4 I understand why you say that.

5 But actually, you also need to consider all the old people.

b 🎧 **44** Listen and check your answers.

6 Listen and respond debating issues

🎧 **45** Listen to five people expressing their views. Respond with your own words. Then compare your response with the model answer that follows.

1

I find it amazing that no one has developed the area around the canal. It has such potential.

I agree. It's an obvious area for development. What they should do is make a nice area with shops and restaurants.

5e Big cities, big problems

Writing an opinion essay

1 Read the paragraphs from an opinion essay on the topic 'Is urban sprawl a good thing?' Put the paragraphs in the correct order.

1 .... 2 .... 3 .... 4 ....

A

In the heart of the city, on the other hand, life for residents is tougher. They have no garden, there is more pollution, and probably also more crime and poverty. In addition, rents are high. Because of this, more and more people are moving to the suburbs and the city keeps spreading.

B

In 1965, George Fieraru predicted, 'By the year 2000, the area in the north-eastern United States between Boston and Washington DC, a distance of 450 miles, will form one big megalopolis.' He was wrong, but not far wrong! Towns and cities continue to grow outwards. As a result, the space they occupy grows bigger and the rural areas around them grow smaller. This is known as 'urban sprawl'. It seems to be a natural phenomenon, but is it a good one and should it be stopped?

C

There is nothing wrong with wanting to have the best of both town and country, but unless planners do something to reverse this trend, our city centres will eventually die. The only answer is to limit urban sprawl and focus our efforts on making our city centres more pleasant places to live.

D

Urban sprawl takes place because people want to have the benefits of both city and country. In the suburbs, they can have a nice home, a piece of land, a peaceful and safe environment, and convenient transport links into the city where they work.

2 Which of the following techniques does the writer use to begin the essay?

a giving a dramatic example of the problem (perhaps from your own experience)

b giving some statistics that illustrate the seriousness of the problem

c quoting what someone (often famous) has said about this problem

3 Rewrite the opening sentence(s) to this essay using one of the other techniques.

4 Find expressions in the essay that mean the same as the following.

1 As well as this (para A) ....

2 Consequently (para A and B)

....

....

3 in contrast (para A) ....

5 Writing skill linking words

a Look at the examples (a–d). Notice that the linking phrases need to be followed by a noun or the -*ing* form of the verb.

a **In addition to** this, cities are becoming more polluted.

b **As well as** this growth outwards, there is also more congestion in cities.

c **Because of** growing outwards, cities are taking up valuable green space.

d **As a result of** cities growing outwards, we are losing valuable green space.

b Rewrite the sentences using the linking phrases given.

1 The house comes with three acres of land and a swimming pool.

As well as ....

2 People have moved out of the centre because crime has risen.

As a result of ....

3 We have a good bus service and excellent roads into the city centre.

In addition to ....

4 We are starting to redevelop city centres because there are restrictions on building on green spaces.

Because of ....

Glossary

urban sprawl (n) / ˈɜː(r)bən sprɔːl/ expansion of a city through development (negative meaning)

Wordbuilding adverb + adjective

1 Choose the TWO adverbs that collocate with each adjective.

Adverbs	Adjectives
1 badly / well / seriously	prepared
2 shortly /short-term / long-term	unemployed
3 lastly / newly / well	built
4 greatly / highly / well	educated
5 quietly / softly / highly	confident
6 poorly / cleverly / highly	designed
7 culturally / greatly / socially	mixed
8 reasonably / poorly / extremely	well-off

2 Complete these sentences using adverb-adjective collocations from Exercise 1.

1 It's very difficult for .... people to get back into work, because they lose confidence.

2 I wouldn't say they are rich, but they are .... compared to other people.

3 He didn't say so, but I think he was .... that the project would be a success.

4 It's a very .... building. Even though it holds a lot of people, you never feel that it is overcrowded.

5 I'm afraid that I was .... for the meeting. Everyone else had read all the background information.

6 London is a very .... city. You can find people from most parts of the world living there.

7 They have a .... workforce. Eighty per cent of their employees are university graduates.

8 Most of the buildings in the area date back to the last century, although there are a few .... houses.

Learning skills critical thinking when you read

3 It is useful to apply critical thinking techniques when you read a text. Read these steps:

- Always scan the text quickly to get a general idea of the topic before you read it in detail.
- Look at who wrote it and for whom. Think about why they wrote the text.
- Read it carefully and note down the main points.
- Does the author develop a particular theme or argument? Is this presented logically?
- Do you agree or disagree with the argument?
- What other knowledge about the subject do you have? Does it fit with the arguments in the text?
- If you are interested in the topic, follow up your reading by researching more about the subject.

4 Look at the article on page 58 of the Student's Book again. Use the critical thinking techniques in Exercise 3 above and write your answers.

Check!

5 Do the quiz. You can find the answers in Student's Book Unit 5.

Quiz

1 Which of these words does NOT describe a type of development?
   a personal
   b economic
   c growth

2 Which of these is NOT in Dubai?
   a the world's tallest building
   b the world's biggest shopping mall
   c the world's busiest airport

3 Kerala is a happy society because the government has invested a lot in:
   a agriculture.
   b political involvement.
   c health and education.

4 Which of these types of behaviour are characteristic of teenagers?
   a seeking new and risky experiences
   b doing things without thinking
   c preferring the company of their peers

5 Which of these phrases has the same meaning as *In addition*?
   a Then again
   b Furthermore
   c Consequently

Unit 6 Alternative travel

6a Staycations

Listening personal experiences

1 🔊 **46** Listen to four people talking about their idea of a staycation. Choose the thing (a–h) that is most important for them in a staycation. There are two extra items.

    a writing a staycation plan

    b going back to a simpler way of life   Speaker 1 ___

    c changing your routine   Speaker 2 ___

    d getting help at home   Speaker 3 ___

    e spoiling yourself

    f filling the days with stimulating new experiences   Speaker 4 ___

2 🔊 **46** Listen again. Choose the activity (a–f) each speaker suggests. There are two extra activities.

    a spending family time just chatting and playing

    b taking your children on day trips   Speaker 1 ___

    c learning a new sport   Speaker 2 ___

    d enjoying the experience of shopping for food   Speaker 3 ___

    e eating out often   Speaker 4 ___

    f getting a little exercise each day

3 Look at the phrases in bold from the listening. Choose the correct definition.

    1 By staying at home, you're not necessarily going to relax and **switch off**.

        a forget about work

        b feel out of touch with the world

        c get more rest

    2 I don't want to **be prescriptive**, but you must make some rules.

        a frighten you

        b tell you exactly what to do

        c be funny

    3 My idea of a staycation is to **pamper myself**.

        a go to the health club

        b spoil myself

        c do healthy things

    4 I organized things to do every day. Maybe my family thought I **overdid** it.

        a wanted to impress people

        b organized too much

        c spent a lot of money

    5 Modern life shouldn't **dictate** your routine.

        a interfere with

        b destroy

        c control

Grammar negative forms

4 Rewrite the phrases in bold in the negative form.

    1 **Let's pretend** that just by staying at home, you're going to relax.

    2 **Answer** the phone.

    3 **You have to do** a big weekly shop.

    4 It would be easier **to go** to the gym every day.

    5 **I think it's extravagant**, because I'm spending less than I would on holiday.

    6 Did we do too many activities? **I hope so.**

    7 I tried **to let the children know** I was worried.

    8 So **you really must let** modern life dictate what you do too much.

5 Rewrite the sentences using negative forms and the words given.

1 I'm sorry, no.
_____ AFRAID

2 It doesn't seem to me to be a great idea.
_____ THINK

3 We shouldn't do anything to upset them.
_____ LET

4 I'm worried that I gave her the wrong impression.
_____ HOPE

5 You can give the book back to me when you like.
_____
_____ HAVE / IMMEDIATELY

6 Don't be late, please.
_____ TRY

7 It is forbidden to take food into the library.
_____ MUST

8 No one there knew the answer, not even the teacher.
_____ NONE

Vocabulary travel

6 Complete the description of a holiday. Write one word in each space.

We had a great holiday, thanks. Up until September, I had only had two days
¹_____ all year. We booked a self-
²_____ apartment in a little village in Pelion in the north of Greece. Pelion has lovely ³_____ : wooded hills leading down to beautiful little coves and a crystal clear sea. Our apartment was in a village a little way up in the hills with a fantastic
⁴_____ of the sea. We flew with one of the low-budget ⁵_____ – I think our return flights were less than £100 each. We only took hand ⁶_____ with us because on low-budget flights they charge extra for each bag you take. Then we rented a car to get us from the airport to our accommodation. It was quite a long
⁷_____ but we went through very pretty ⁸_____ . Coming back was expensive, though. The drive to the airport
⁹_____ about three hours longer because of roadworks. So the car hire company charged us for an extra half day. Then the airline said my ¹⁰_____ was too big and it would have to go in the hold – for an extra £80! I couldn't believe it.

Vocabulary holiday activities

7 Complete these holiday activities. The first letter is given for you.

1 lying on the beach s_____

2 going on a g_____ tour of the city

3 buying s_____ to take home for friends

4 s_____ in the sea with a mask and flippers

5 s_____ in a historic city

6 r_____ on a segway

7 e_____ o_____ in nice restaurants

8 b_____ to find shells and other interesting things

8 Dictation staycations

🎵 **47** Listen to a travel expert describing the trend in staycations. He makes four points. Write the words that you hear. Do you agree with him?

1 In tough economic times, _____
_____
_____

2 However, they _____
_____
_____

3 You don't have to _____
_____
_____

4 I don't think _____
_____
_____

6b Why volunteer?

Vocabulary travel

1 Put the words in order to describe things to do before going on a trip.

1 pass / off / boarding / print

2 lotion / and / guidebook / suntan / buy

3 up to date / insurance / is / travel / check

4 details / write / contact / down

5 before / vaccinations / get / travelling

6 is / valid / check / passport

Reading volunteering

2 Read the information from a volunteering website. Complete the notes about the short-term voluntary roles.

Type of work: [1] ....

Skills and experience required: [2] ....

Length of stay: [3] ....

Costs: [4] ....

Why volunteer?

Volunteering is one of the most rewarding ways you can make a real difference to people who live in very tough circumstances. Most people join us because they want to give something back. In doing so, they find they get much more in return.

We send volunteers rather than money. We work on lasting, sustainable solutions. And volunteers are how we do it. Nothing compares with the satisfaction of practical, life-changing achievements.

Our short-term roles give experienced professionals the opportunity to make a real contribution to the fight against poverty. You'll face fresh challenges, develop valuable new skills, and experience another culture in a way few people have the opportunity to.

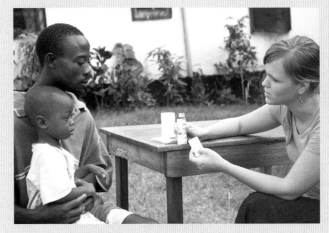

Who can be a short-term volunteer?
Our positions tend to be consultancy-type roles, which are designed to achieve a specific goal or complete a particular project, so they require highly skilled professionals who can hit the ground running. The majority of short-term roles last between four and six months.

For most of our roles, you will need at least five years' experience in your area of work, be able to stay for six months, and be ready to leave for your volunteering job within eighteen months of applying. We match volunteers to the jobs they are most professionally suited to. It helps if you are flexible about where you are willing to work.

How we'll support you
This isn't 'voluntourism' – you don't have to pay to volunteer with us. We take care of all your expenses, from flights and insurance through to visas and accommodation. We even give you a local living allowance. For more information, see our volunteering FAQs.

The skills we're looking for
We are currently looking for short-term volunteers in the following sectors: agricultural specialists, business and management specialists, financial specialists, fundraisers, IT specialists, researchers, other specialist and one-off roles.

If you don't yet have the level of experience to be able to do a short-term role, you can look at the long-term opportunities in your area of work.

3 Read the information again and choose the correct option (a–c).

1 People who 'want to give something back' (para 1) means people who want to:
   a repay the organization for giving them a job.
   b give money to the organization.
   c make a contribution to society.

2 Short-term volunteer jobs are open to people:
   a who like project work.
   b with some work expertise.
   c who have already worked as consultants.

3 'Hit the ground running' (para 3) means:
   a start work without any preparation.
   b be very adaptable.
   c use your intelligence.

4 When placing people, the organization especially takes into account a volunteer's:
   a wishes.
   b willingness to work.
   c work background.

5 Which of the following volunteer costs does the organization NOT mention?
   a travel
   b day-to-day expenses
   c loss of regular income

6 The article suggests that long-terms posts are better for people who:
   a are less experienced travellers.
   b have less work experience.
   c are less confident.

4 Read the information again and find adjectives that mean:

1 satisfying (para 1) _____
2 difficult (para 1) _____
3 long-term (para 2) _____
4 new (para 3) _____
5 right for (para 5) _____
6 able to adapt (para 5) _____

Grammar question forms

5 Look at the questions that a potential volunteer asks. Complete them with question tags.

1 A: You don't organize two-week volunteer vacations, _____ ?
   B: No, we don't.

2 A: But the work would be suitable for a gap-year student, _____ ?
   B: Well, no. It's aimed at an older age group.

3 A: It isn't suitable for my eighteen-year-old daughter, then, _____ ?
   B: No, I'm afraid it isn't.

4 A: But you used to take younger volunteers, _____ ?
   B: Yes, but our policy has changed.

5 A: So, as a teacher, there might be possibilities for me to volunteer, _____ ?
   B: Absolutely, for a longer-term post.

6 A: And I'd have to be flexible about where and when I could go, _____ ?
   B: Well, of course, flexibility helps.

6 Rewrite the questions using different types of question forms. Use the question form in brackets.

1 What kind of expenses do you cover? (indirect question)
   Can you tell _____ ?

2 Would it harm my future career to take time away from work to volunteer? (indirect question)
   Do you think _____ ?

3 Would you like to use your skills to help others? (negative question)
   _____ ?

4 Are there organizations which offer long-term volunteering jobs for inexperienced people? (indirect question)
   Do you know _____ ?

5 Is it a bit selfish to volunteer just because you want to travel? (tag question)
   _____ ?

6 Is it more interesting to see another country as a volunteer rather than as a tourist? (*surely* question)
   _____ ?

7 Pronunciation intonation in question forms

🎧 **48** Look at the questions. Does the intonation rise (R) or fall (F) at the end? Then listen and check.

		R	F
1	It's a fantastic idea, isn't it?	☐	☐
2	Wouldn't it be great if everyone did this?	☐	☐
3	Have you heard of VSO?	☐	☐
4	You can't really make that kind of long-term commitment, can you?	☐	☐
5	Didn't you do some volunteering when you were a student?	☐	☐
6	I don't have the right qualifications, do I?	☐	☐
7	Do you know any other organizations like VSO?	☐	☐
8	It would be interesting to talk to someone who's done it, wouldn't it?	☐	☐

6c Unusual trips

Listening a cruise with a difference

1 💿 **49** You are going to listen to a review of a cruise. Look at these words. Tick (✓) the items you would expect to find on a typical cruise ship. Then listen and compare which items are on *NG Endeavour* cruises.

- ☐ shops
- ☐ a swimming pool
- ☐ a casino
- ☐ a library
- ☐ professional photographers
- ☐ sightseeing excursions
- ☐ kayaking trips
- ☐ shopping trips
- ☐ wildlife excursions
- ☐ expert guides

2 💿 **49** Complete the table with the information you heard about the cruise. Then listen again and check.

Name of ship	NG Endeavour
Type of ship	a converted ¹ .... trawler
Facilities	a swimming pool, a ² .... deck, a library, a ³ .... centre, a relaxing ⁴ ....
Destination	Galápagos ⁵ ....
Equipment	⁶ .... and Zodiacs
On-board staff	photographers and expert ⁷ .... guides
Cost	⁸ .... per ⁹ ....
Food	good ¹⁰ .... food

3 How does the reviewer describe the *NG Endeavour* cruises? Choose the correct option.

1 luxurious / comfortable
2 educational / entertaining
3 adventurous / safe
4 cheap / expensive

4 Look at the audioscript on page 120 and find words with the following meanings.

1 smooth and attractive (para 1)
   ....

2 metal structures used in construction for lifting heavy objects (para 2) ....

3 a centre or main residence (para 3)
   ....

4 the only one of its kind (para 4)
   ....

5 far away from towns or cities (para 5)
   ....

Word focus *mind*

5 Rewrite the expressions in bold using expressions with *mind*.

1 **If you were thinking of a cruise**, try one of Lindblad's expeditions. (have in mind)

2 **If a bit of danger and excitement are not a problem for you**, Lindblad cruises are perfect. (don't mind)

3 I meant to book this holiday, but **I've been too busy thinking about other things**. (on my mind)

4 **Remember that** these are not typical cruises. (bear in mind)

5 I used to think that cruises were for the retired, **but I've got a different opinion** now. (change one's mind)

6 **I want to go** on one of their cruises, **but it's quite expensive**. (be in two minds)

6 Grammar extra negative expressions

a Look at these negative expressions.
   a **Don't** judge a book by its cover.
   b **No** problem.
   c **It doesn't** matter.

b Complete these common expressions using the correct negative forms.

1 .... worry.
2 .... worries.
3 .... make sense.
4 .... way!
5 .... say a word.
6 .... work like that.

6d Couch surfing

Real life getting around

1 🎵 **50** Complete the sentences using prepositions. Then listen to a conversation between two friends and check.

1 I'll be coming _____ on the five o'clock train.
2 I can't pick you _____ , I'm afraid.
3 How do I get _____ Sara's Café?
4 Just hop _____ any bus from the station.
5 Look _____ for the pier and get off there.
6 You'll see the café _____ your right.
7 If I get held _____ , I'll call you.
8 I'll come _____ and meet you.

2 🎵 **50** Listen again and answer the questions.

1 Why can't Steve meet Joe at the station?

_____

2 How will Joe get to the meeting point?

_____

3 Where do they arrange to meet in the end?

_____

3 Rewrite the sentences so that they have the same meaning. Use the words in brackets.

1 The easiest option is to take the bus.
_____ (thing)

2 Another possibility is to take a taxi.
_____ (alternatively)

3 I can get there on my own.
_____ (way)

4 It only takes fifteen minutes by bus.
_____ (ride)

5 I'm arriving by train.
_____ (coming)

6 If I am delayed, I'll let you know.
_____ (held)

4 Choose the correct word to complete the situations.

crossing	drive	flight	ride (x2)	walk

1 It's a twenty-minute _____ . (car)
2 It's a two-hour _____ . (plane)
3 It's a fifteen-minute _____ . (bus)
4 It's a twenty-minute _____ . (foot)
5 It's a ten-minute _____ . (taxi)
6 It's a one-hour _____ . (ferry boat)

5 Pronunciation intonation in sentences with two clauses

a 🎵 **51** Match the sentence halves. Then listen and check.

1 I'd prefer to drive,
2 It's not difficult to find,
3 I could come and meet you,
4 The bus is cheap,
5 You could take a taxi,

a but I don't finish work until 6.00 p.m.
b but it's quite a long way from the station.
c but it's a very scenic walk.
d but the car is behaving strangely.
e but it makes a lot of stops on the way.

b 🎵 **51** Practise saying the sentences using the correct intonation.

6 Listen and respond getting around

🎵 **52** Listen to a friend asking you for directions to your house from the town centre. Respond with your own words. Then compare your response with the model answer that follows.

1

> Hi there. I'm coming in on the train tomorrow at two o'clock. What's the best way to get to your house from there?

> The easiest thing is to take the bus.

6e A disappointed customer

Writing a letter/email of complaint

1 Read the letter of complaint and answer the questions.

1 What is the woman's complaint?

2 What action does she want to be taken?

24 Clifford Gardens
Oxford
OX3 2FG

U-Fly Airlines
108 Pembroke Road
London
W8 7NP

Dear Sir/Madam

I am writing to register a complaint about having to pay extra charges to your airline on a recent flight to Spain (UZ485 from London to Seville on 3rd May). I feel that these charges were unjust.

At the time that I booked this flight, I read the terms about luggage carefully. The terms clearly stated that each passenger's hand luggage allowance was one bag measuring no more than 56 x 45 x 25cm and weighing up to 10 kilograms.

On arrival at check-in, I informed the member of the ground crew that my bag met these regulations, but she insisted that the coat that I was wearing should be placed in the bag. I attempted to pack the coat into my bag, but it would not fit, so I was instructed that I would have to pay £30 if I wished to take it onto the plane.

I was concerned that I was delaying other passengers, and consequently I opted to pay the money. Otherwise, I would certainly have disputed the charge, as I am now doing. It is perfectly reasonable to wear a coat onto a plane.

Given these circumstances, I would ask you firstly to refund the £30 to me and secondly to investigate the matter so that you can ensure that other passengers do not encounter the same problem.

Yours faithfully
Amelia Doyle

2 Answer these questions.

1 Where is the writer writing from?

2 What is her relationship to the recipient of the letter?

3 What is the tone of the letter (e.g. formal/semi-formal)?

3 Writing skill formal language

a Find formal phrases in the letter with the same meaning as these less formal words.

1 complain
2 unfair
3 said
4 told
5 put
6 tried
7 wanted
8 chose
9 this situation
10 look into

b Rewrite the first paragraph of this letter of complaint using more formal language. Use these verbs to help you. You can change other words too.

consist	give	register	regret	serve
state	suffer			

Dear Sir/Madam
I'm writing to complain about the meal we got on our flight home last week – flight UZ332. On the booking confirmation it said that we would have breakfast and lunch. Well, breakfast was just a cup of tea and lunch was a tuna sandwich. By itself, this wouldn't have been a problem, but both my husband and I got food poisoning from the sandwich.

4 Write the final paragraph of the letter, demanding some action from the airline.

Wordbuilding phrasal verbs with *in* and *out*

1 Complete the phrasal verbs using *in* and *out*.

1 Do **drop** _____ and see us the next time you're in town.

2 Stefan **dropped** _____ of college last year because he wanted to travel round the world.

3 Philippa and Sarah used to be business partners but they **fell** _____ over how to develop the business.

4 Chris **fell** _____ with the wrong crowd at college and started missing lectures.

5 Ben is **taking** Greta _____ to that new Thai restaurant tonight.

6 Sorry. Can you speak a little more slowly? I couldn't **take** it all _____ .

7 I'll **look** _____ and see my parents on my way home to make sure they're OK.

8 **Look** _____ ! You're going to bang your head on that door.

9 Is your old car still going? I thought it would have **given** _____ years ago.

10 I'm trying not to eat sweets, but I **gave** _____ when Kacey offered me some of her homemade chocolate cake.

2 Match the phrasal verbs from Exercise 1 with the definitions (a–j).

a have a disagreement _____

b absorb (information) _____

c pay someone a (short) visit _____

d pay someone a (short) visit to check they are all right _____

e become part of a social group _____

f be careful _____

g stop fighting against something _____

h arrange a social date with _____

i leave a course before it is finished _____

j stop working or functioning _____

Learning skills writing in English

3 Look at the diagram showing the important elements of writing (in the next column). Complete the diagram with these elements.

spelling   link the ideas   reason for writing
examples

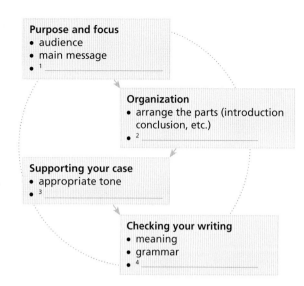

Purpose and focus
- audience
- main message
- 1 _____

Organization
- arrange the parts (introduction conclusion, etc.)
- 2 _____

Supporting your case
- appropriate tone
- 3 _____

Checking your writing
- meaning
- grammar
- 4 _____

4 Look at the letter of complaint in Exercise 1 on page 50. Answer the questions.

1 Why is the formal tone appropriate in this case?

_____

2 What are the three main elements the letter includes?

_____

3 What phrases does the writer use to link the different ideas?

_____

4 What tone does the writer use?

_____

5 What details does the writer give to make her case more persuasive?

_____

Check!

5 Answer the questions. All the answers are in Student's Book Unit 6.

1 How did Karen Ash have a Japanese holiday without leaving home?

2 What is the word for the activity that combines charity work with a holiday?

3 Where can you pay to have an uncomfortable night and be treated unkindly?

4 Where can you imagine you are in an art gallery?

5 What's a way to travel from place to place without ever paying for a bed to sleep in?

7a Child behaviour

Listening growing up

1 🎧 **53** Listen to four people talking about growing up and child behaviour. Match the speakers (1–4) with the topic they are talking about (a–f). There are two extra topics.

Speaker 1 ....
Speaker 2 ....
Speaker 3 ....
Speaker 4 ....

a Being the youngest in the family
b Being the eldest
c Learning from other children
d Competition between siblings
e Home schooling
f Discipline in the home

Glossary
intervene (v) /ˌɪntəˈviːn/ get involved
sibling (n) /ˈsɪblɪŋ/ a brother or sister

2 🎧 **53** Listen again. Write the number of the speaker (1–4) next to the view they are expressing.

a Family arguments are perfectly healthy. ....
b The best results are when parents leave children to learn for themselves. ....
c Having to fight to get your parents' attention can have a positive effect. ....
d Children need to mix with lots of other children. ....
e Your position in the family – e.g. first child, second child – is significant. ....
f Parents should try to be less involved in their children's upbringing. ....

3 Look at the words and phrases in bold from the interviews and choose the correct definition.

1 Schools don't **stretch** children enough.
   a discipline
   b challenge
   c educate

2 I'm sure they **mean well**, but they're missing the point.
   a have good intentions
   b have good ideas
   c have good qualities

3 Children often **squabble** over toys.
   a have small arguments
   b lose interest
   c make friendships

4 Eldest children are organizing and **bossy** types.
   a showing leadership qualities
   b independent
   c telling others what to do

5 Younger children are often the **clowns** of the family.
   a ones who aren't taken seriously
   b ones who like to joke
   c the less intelligent ones

6 It's normal just to leave the children to **get on with it**.
   a manage by themselves
   b make friends with each other
   c grow up

Grammar zero and first conditionals

4 Choose the correct option to complete the sentences.

1 In the UK, the law states that you *are / will be* allowed to teach children at home if you *provide / will provide* them with an 'efficient, full-time education'.

2 The law also says that children *don't / won't* have to be with other children when they *are / will be* taught at home.

3 People who criticize home schooling say children will not learn good social skills, if they *don't / won't* have the company of other children. And I agree. If I *decide / will decide* to home school my children, I *make / will make* sure they have plenty of contact with people their own age.

4 There are so many different books for parents. If you *try / will try* to follow all the different psychologists' advice, you *end / will end* up being a very confused parent!

5 I am the youngest child in my family and I don't agree with the experts who say that when you *are / will be* the youngest you *have / will have* an easier life.

5 Complete the conversations. Use the correct form of the verb in brackets.

1 A: Can you help me with my homework?
   B: Yes, but you _____ (feel) better about it, if you _____ (manage) to do it by yourself.

2 A: Can I borrow your bicycle?
   B: You can, as long as you _____ (promise) to look after it. I only got it last week.

3 A: Where are you going to stay?
   B: I _____ (reserve) a room at the Old Bank Hotel unless it _____ (be) full.

4 A: It's so busy in the office with only two of us here.
   B: Yes, but I'm sure things _____ (get) calmer after everyone _____ (return) from holiday.

5 A: Can I get you a coffee?
   B: No, thanks, I _____ (just / read) the newspaper while I _____ (wait).

6 A: Have you heard anything back from the owners of the house?
   B: No, I haven't. But I soon as I _____ (hear), I _____ (let) you know.

7 A: I think Vicky stands a good chance of winning a prize in the short story competition.
   B: I think so too. And she says that if she _____ (win), she _____ (take) us all out to dinner.

8 A: Will you carry on trying to look for a job in London?
   B: Yes, I will – until I _____ (find) one.

9 A: What are we going to do for dinner tonight?
   B: I _____ (cook) something if I _____ (get) home early enough.

10 A: Does your sister have children?
   B: Not yet. She says she _____ (not / have) children while she _____ (live) in such a small apartment.

Vocabulary raising children: verbs

6 Complete the sentences using the correct verbs. The first letter has been given for you.

Hannah: My father worked abroad for most of my childhood so we were [1] **b**_____ up by my mother. When he came home, he used to [2] **s**_____ us quite a lot, buying us presents and taking us out. He never [3] **p**_____ us if we were naughty, because he wanted to enjoy his time with us. He left it to my mum to [4] **t**_____ us off if we were naughty. That was tough on her, because we used to [5] **d**_____ her quite a lot – playing outside when she had told us not to.

Laura: It's difficult being a single parent looking after your children. You are always [6] **n**_____ them to do things, when really you want to enjoy the time you have with them. My elder sister [7] **r**_____ against my parents completely and went off to live in London when she was seventeen.

Marco: It isn't easy being a parent. My own kids are always asking me to buy them things, but I try not to [8] **g**_____ in to their demands. Of course, when they do something good, I might [9] **r**_____ them with a present!

7 Dictation raising children

🎧 **54** Listen to a psychologist talking about bringing up children and complete the paragraphs. Which aspect of bringing up children do you agree with most?

Everything depends on _____ .

In other words, what _____
_____ ?

Do you want them _____ ?

If so, _____
_____ .

Or do you want them to be successful individuals? If so, _____
_____ .

Or is it important that they are good family members? Then _____
_____ .

7b Globalization of the food market

Reading global food

1 Read the article. What effect has the globalization of food had?
  a Food is now cheaper than it was before.
  b The food on our tables has become more international.
  c Poorer people can now eat as well as richer people.

2 Read the article again and answer the questions.

  1 The author thinks that the weekly family menu in Britain fifty years ago:
     a was very boring for those who had to eat it.
     b used food resources carefully.
     c was not very nutritious.

  2 The main difference with a weekly family menu in Britain these days is that:
     a people eat food that is in season.
     b people have more money to eat out.
     c there is a greater choice of food.

  3 The phrase 'standardization of taste' means:
     a we all eat similar things.
     b everything tastes more and more the same.
     c each type of food doesn't taste as strong as it did in the past.

  4 The main reason that the price of food has increased globally is:
     a people in fast-developing countries want more Western-style food.
     b climate change has badly affected food production.
     c the general economic depression.

  5 Higher food prices have caused people in the West to:
     a eat less meat.
     b not eat in restaurants.
     c reduce the amount they spend on food.

GLOBALIZATION OF THE FOOD MARKET

Globalization has had a huge impact on eating habits all over the world. From the UK to Kenya to China, the food we eat today is determined by global markets and world economic events.

If you go back fifty years, a typical working family in Britain ate the same things every week – not that anyone complained about it. The weekly menu was built around the Sunday roast, when a large piece of meat – beef or lamb, for example – was served with seasonal vegetables as a treat. On the following days, people used to eat leftovers from this 'feast' in a way that clearly avoided waste. On Monday they would have cold cuts of meat and on Tuesday a dish made from the remains, such as shepherd's pie. Wednesday and Thursday were less predictable, but Friday was 'Fish and Chips' day. Saturday was usually sausage and mash because this was quick and easy, and then it was back to the Sunday roast again.

Look at today's average weekly family menu in Britain and there is no comparison. For a start, there is no average: the element of predictability has disappeared, because what is on offer now is not just British but international cuisine. Chinese stir-fry on Sunday, Italian lasagne on Wednesday, Mexican tortillas on Thursday. Secondly, the season is no longer a factor. If I want strawberries in December or asparagus in March, I can buy them, because even if it's not the season to grow them in the UK, it is in South Africa or Chile. Eating out is not the exceptional treat it used to be. It's fairly normal to eat out at least once a week and to have a takeaway – perhaps a curry – when you can't be bothered to cook.

But while globalization may have brought more variety to our table, at the same time global food brands have brought a standardization of taste, particularly in snack foods and fast foods. You can buy a Kit Kat anywhere from Berne to Beijing, and no one is surprised any more when they see McDonald's in some small town far from the USA.

This demand for Western foods, such as hamburgers and pizza, in countries where there is rapid economic development has had a dramatic effect on the price of wheat and other basic foods. Add to this crop failures from bad weather conditions and the result is that we are all paying more for our food. In the West, this may cause us some inconvenience: eating chicken, which is less expensive, instead of beef for example, or cutting back on the number of times we eat out, but in under-developed countries the effect has been much more damaging. For a poor family in Kenya who are used to a diet of corn, rice and beans with meat maybe once or twice a week, the choice is not between goat or chicken, but rather rice with beans or rice without beans.

Glossary
mash (n) /mæʃ/ mashed potatoes
treat (n) /triːt/ something special to reward people

Grammar *usually, used to, would, be used to* and *get used to*

3 Choose the correct option according to the article on page 54.

1 Fifty years ago, families in Britain *usually eat / were used to eating / used to eat* the same thing every week.

2 People didn't complain, because they *weren't used to seeing / didn't get used to seeing / wouldn't see* food from all over in the world.

3 British families *were used to using / got used to using / would use* the Sunday roast to make meals for the next two days.

4 On Fridays they *usually have / were used to having / would have* fish and chips.

5 Today people in Britain *are used to eating / get used to eating / used to eat* a variety of international foods.

6 Since food became globalized, people *usually eat / have got used to eating / would eat* whatever they want, whether it is in season or not.

7 They *usually eat out / got used to eating out / used to eat out* at least once a week.

8 Nowadays, people *usually see / are used to seeing / got used to seeing* McDonald's everywhere in the world.

9 In the past, people in Kenya *are used to eating / got used to eating / used to eat* rice, corn, beans and a little meat.

10 Nowadays, in tougher times, they *usually eat / are used to eating / got used to eating* just beans and rice.

4 Read about an English person living 100 years ago. Which of the underlined verbs can be replaced with *used to, would* or *was/were used to*? Write the alternative.

'We [1] <u>didn't cook</u> on a stove, because we didn't have one. We [2] <u>cooked</u> everything over a fire. For example, if we [3] <u>wanted</u> to cook sausages, we [4] <u>hung</u> them on hooks over the fire. But if it [5] <u>was</u> a special occasion and we had a lot of things to cook, then we had to take it down the road to the hotel which [6] <u>had</u> a proper oven and for a few pennies they [7] <u>cooked</u> it for us. It seems strange now, but we [8] <u>did</u> that whenever all the family got round the table.'

1	*didn't use to cook*	5	
2		6	
3		7	
4		8	

5 Pronunciation /juː/ and /uː/

a 🔘 **55** Listen to these words. Write the words in the table.

blue	consume	fortune	humanity	humour
lunar	menu	rude	suit	truce	used
usually				

/uː/	/juː/

b 🔘 **56** Listen and check your answers to Exercise 5a.

Vocabulary food and eating habits

6 Look at what these four people ate for lunch. Which of the following did they have? Write snack food (SF), dairy product (D), protein-rich food (P), fresh fruit and vegetables (F) and soft drinks (SD).

1 **Simon**
tuna sandwich

packet of crisps

2 **Kerry**
yoghurt
grapes

3 **Will**
mixed salad
bag of peanuts

can of cola

4 **Katie**
hamburger
strawberry
milkshake

7c Body language

Listening Desmond Morris

1 🔊 **57** Listen to a description of the work of Desmond Morris. Are the sentences true (T) or false (F)?

1 Desmond Morris trained as a zoologist and a psychologist.
2 More than ninety per cent of human communication is made using speech.
3 The first example describes the body language of Desmond Morris and a radio presenter.
4 Postural echo involves imitating someone's facial expressions.
5 In the second situation (the job interview), it would be right to use postural echo.
6 Leaning back in your chair shows that you feel in control.

2 🔊 **57** Look at the diagrams (a–d) and answer the questions. Then listen again and check.

1 In the first situation, how are Desmond Morris and the presenter sitting? Choose the correct diagram.
2 How should the boss and the interviewee be sitting? Choose the correct diagram.

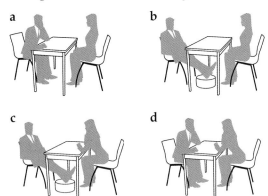

a   b
c   d

3 🔊 **57** Choose the correct option to complete the sentences. Then listen again and check.

1 Morris's lifelong interest has been human *as much as / rather* than animal behaviour.
2 *Unlike / Like* the traditional experts in human behaviour, he is not so interested in what people say, but rather in what they do.
3 In fact, he gives *a lot of / little* attention to human speech.
4 In another situation, though, *no / such* postural echo might be inappropriate.
5 *At best, / At worst*, the boss would find it deeply insulting.

4 Pronunciation unstressed syllables

🔊 **58** Look at these words. In each word, the second syllable is unstressed and contains the schwa /ə/ sound. Listen and repeat.

action	common	elder	forward	human
little	other	posture	rather	verbal

Word focus *same* and *different*

5 Complete the conversations with these expressions.

a difference of opinion	no difference
a different tune	the same boat
all the same	the same coin
a different matter	the same thing

1 A: Would you like to do the washing up or the drying up?
   B: I really don't mind. It's _____ to me.
2 A: Why do you think rich people are often so dissatisfied?
   B: I think that earning more and wanting more are two sides of _____ .
3 A: I spent three years at teaching college but I don't feel any more confident in the classroom.
   B: Learning the theory is one thing, actually practising something is _____ .
4 A: What's the difference between *a truck* and *a lorry*?
   B: Well, one is American English and one is British English, but in meaning they're one and _____ .
5 A: Did you have an argument with Emilia?
   B: I wouldn't say it was an argument – just _____ .
6 A: Did you find the rooms in the hotel rather small?
   B: Yes, but it made _____ because we were out sightseeing most of the time.
7 A: Does she still think that golf is an easy sport?
   B: No, now that she's tried it, she's singing _____ .
8 A: They keep giving me more and more work to do. I just don't know how I am supposed to cope.
   B: I know, but try not to worry about it. We're all in _____ .

7d Wedding customs

Vocabulary weddings

1 Write the words for these definitions.

1 a post-wedding holiday ....
2 the party after the wedding ceremony
   ....
3 a pre-wedding party for men only is called a
   '.. do'
4 a covering for the bride's face ....
5 an .... ring shows a promise to be
   married in future
6 the man on his wedding day ....
7 the person who has promised to get married
   ....

Real life describing traditions

2 🔊 **59** Listen to the description of the custom of
dowry-giving and answer the questions.

1 What is a big dowry a sign of?
   ....
2 Why was a woman's dowry of practical
   importance?
   ....
3 Which family normally gives the dowry?
   ....
4 Which family gives the dowry in Nigeria?
   ....
5 What do the guests at a Nigerian engagement
   ceremony do, as well as dancing and having fun?
   ....
6 What two things does a Nigerian dowry consist
   of?
   ....

> **Glossary**
> **dowry** (n) /ˈdaʊri/ property or money given to the groom
> by the bride's family

3 🔊 **59** Complete the sentences with the words in
the box. Then listen again and check.

> customary   marks   occasion   on   place
> rule   symbolizes   traditional

1 Dowry-giving .... different
   things, for example, a sign of wealth.
2 As a .... , in the past, brides
   did not go out to work.
3 It's .... for a dowry to be given
   by the bride's family.
4 The engagement ceremony in Nigeria
   .... the beginning of the
   wedding celebrations.
5 The ceremony is an .... for
   people to have fun.
6 It takes .... on the evening or a
   couple of nights before the wedding itself.
7 It used to be .... for money to
   be thrown at the couple's feet.
8 .... the night of the wedding,
   the bride goes back to her own house.

4 Pronunciation the letter *s*

🔊 **60** Look at these words. Is the 's' sound /s/ or
/z/? Listen and check.

		/s/	/z/			/s/	/z/
1	thing**s**	☐	☐	7	**s**uit	☐	☐
2	hou**se**	☐	☐	8	ki**ss**	☐	☐
3	bride**s**	☐	☐	9	deliver**s**	☐	☐
4	**s**ocial	☐	☐	10	increa**se**	☐	☐
5	**s**ign	☐	☐	11	reali**z**e	☐	☐
6	clothe**s**	☐	☐	12	i**s**	☐	☐

5 Listen and respond describing traditions

🔊 **61** Listen to some questions about wedding
traditions and customs. Respond with your own
words. Then compare your response with the
model answer that follows.

1
> *What does the groom wear
> on his wedding day?*

> *It's traditional for the groom to
> wear a morning suit and a top
> hat, but these days, he can also
> wear an ordinary suit.*

7e Scarlet sails

1 Writing skill adding detail

Read the description of a festival called *Scarlet Sails*. Complete the text with the missing details (a–e).

a in which a prince comes for his loved one in a beautiful ship with red sails

b drinking and dancing

c which is a festival of classical music and dance that runs from May to July

d with bright red sails

e one of the most beautiful cities in the world

2
Read the description again. What adjectives are used to describe these things?

1 Alexander Grin's story:

....

2 the ship, *Secret*:

....

3 the colour of the sails:

....

4 the night of the celebration in general:

.... , ... ,

....

Writing a description

3
Complete this description of a spring festival in Oxford, in the UK, with the correct verbs and nouns. The first letter is given for you.

> **May morning**
>
> May morning in Oxford ¹ t..............
> p.............. every year on 1st May and
> ² m.............. the arrival of spring. The
> celebrations usually ³ b.............. the night
> before and many people stay up all through the
> night waiting for the sunrise. The ⁴ h..............
> of the celebrations are when a crowd
> ⁵ g.............. on a bridge in the city centre to
> listen to a choir singing at the top of Magdalen
> College tower. At 6.00 a.m., the bells ring and
> everyone is quiet. Then the silence is broken by
> the beautiful voices of the choir. When the choir
> has finished, the celebrations begin again with
> singing and ⁶ d.............. .

Scarlet sails

Scarlet Sails is a spectacular celebration in St Petersburg, Russia,
¹ .... – a colourful mixture of parades, concerts and fireworks. It takes place every year in the middle of June and marks the graduation of students from all over Russia and the end of the academic year. It is part of the summer *White Nights* festival,
² .... *Scarlet Sails* is named after a romantic fairytale written in 1917 by the writer Alexander Grin,
³ ....

The festival begins around 11 p.m. at night with a concert and theatrical performance in St Petersburg's Palace Square for all the graduating students. The main focus of the festival are the boats that parade along the Neva River, and crowds gather on the waterfront to watch them. As they go past, fireworks are set off in time to classical music by famous Russian composers. The highlight is the appearance of the ship *Secret*, a magnificent sailing ship ⁴ .... After the parade, which can also be seen on big screens around the city, celebrations continue with other concerts, and
⁵ .... until the dawn arrives at four in the morning. It is a magical night.

Wordbuilding word pairs

1 Make matching pairs. Match the words in box A with their 'pair' in box B.

> **A** bits bride husband food friends
> fun life plans pomp* singing
> suit time

> **B** arrangements ceremony dancing drink
> family games groom pieces soul
> tie trouble wife

> **Glossary**
> ***pomp** (n) /pɒmp/ magnificent display

2 Complete the sentences with matching pairs from Exercise 1.

1 We wanted a simple wedding, without the _____ of a normal wedding.

2 Planning the wedding took ages, but it was worth all the _____ .

3 There's so much to organize at a wedding, including all the _____ that you never think about beforehand.

4 I'm so glad we invited James – he's always the _____ of the party.

5 It was a small wedding. We just invited a few _____ .

6 The woman usually wears a white dress and the man wears a _____ .

Learning skills making full use of your teacher

3 Use your teacher as a resource. Read these tips to help improve your English.

1 Pay attention to the way your teacher pronounces words and phrases and try to imitate them.

2 Every teacher uses certain idiomatic phrases and expressions. Ask them what they mean.

3 Ask the teacher to correct your mistakes, particularly your pronunciation. Even teachers can feel shy about doing this.

4 Ask your teacher what they think your main fault in English is and how you can correct it.

5 Tell your teacher what kinds of books you like to read and ask them to recommend some in English.

6 Make sure that you have the vocabulary you need (e.g. to describe your job). Ask your teacher to supply these words.

4 Answer these questions. Then check with your teacher. Does your teacher agree with you?

1 Can you pronounce these words from Unit 10?
   a disobey
   b dairy
   c future

2 Which one of these do you think you have most difficulty with?
   a using the right tense
   b lack of vocabulary
   c pronouncing things correctly

3 What can you do well in English?
   a study
   b communicate at work
   c get around in a foreign country

Check!

5 Complete these phrasal verbs and idiomatic phrases. You can find all the answers in Student's Book Unit 7.

Quiz Time

1 Try not to give _____ to all your children's demands.

2 We don't eat _____ much these days because restaurants are so expensive.

3 It's very rude to stare _____ your phone at the dinner table.

4 Alex and I had a difference _____ opinion.

5 Bringing _____ children is not easy.

6 I don't mind what you do. It's all the same _____ me.

7 The festival begins _____ a big firework display.

8 It was always my mother not my father who used to tell me _____ if I was naughty.

Unit 8 Hopes and ambitions

8a Fulfilling your dreams

Vocabulary goals and ambitions

1 Complete the sentences about goals and ambitions. Use nouns and verbs. The first letter is given for you.

1 They're trying to raise money for charity. Their t_____ is £5,000.

2 I hope your dreams c_____ true one day.

3 It's natural to try to l_____ up to your parents' expectations, but it isn't always easy.

4 I'm sorry, but what exactly is the a_____ of this exercise? I don't see the point.

5 My brother always says that I don't h_____ any ambition, but it's just that I don't know yet what I want to do.

6 It took her twenty years, but she finally has a_____ her goal of becoming an author.

Listening ambitions

2 🔊 **62** Listen to two people talking about their ambitions. Complete the table.

Speaker	Their ambition	What they were doing before
1 Rhea		
2 Sasha		

3 🔊 **62** Listen to the speakers again. Choose the correct option to complete each statement (a–c).

1 Rhea's achievements include:
   a raising children.
   b running a company.
   c building her own home.

2 The aim of the volunteer programme in Rwanda was to teach children using:
   a acting and drama.
   b useful work tasks.
   c games and play.

3 Rhea says before she arrived at the school the children:
   a didn't learn much.
   b didn't move about much.
   c didn't pay much attention to the teacher.

4 When she left college, Sasha thought that art would probably be:
   a her career.
   b something she did in her free time.
   c her whole life.

5 She moved to Glasgow because:
   a that's where her friends were.
   b it was the centre of the art world.
   c it wasn't so expensive to live there.

6 In Sasha's gallery they have shown:
   a their own work.
   b only local artists' work.
   c some well-known artists' work.

4 Match the words in bold used by the speakers with the correct definition (a or b).

1 I wanted to help people in a more **meaningful** way.
   a wanting to do good
   b significant

2 I was very **fortunate**
   a happy   b lucky

3 I have found my **calling**
   a the job that was right for me
   b a job I was good at

4 a nice space in an old **warehouse**
   a a building where goods are kept
   b a factory building

5 had the idea of **setting up** a gallery
   a building   b establishing

6 it just **took off** from there
   a became famous   b became successful

Grammar second, third and mixed conditionals

5 Complete the sentences about Rhea and Sasha. Put the verbs in the correct form. Use second, third and mixed conditionals.

1 If Rhea _____ (feel) that working in insurance was a more meaningful job, she _____ (carry) on doing that job.

2 If Rhea's friend _____ (not / tell) her about the volunteer programme, she _____ (not / be) a teacher trainer now.

3 If the children in the school she visited _____ (still / learn) using the old methods, they _____ (probably / be) less interested in learning.

4 If Glasgow _____ (be) an expensive city to live in, Sasha _____ (not/ move) there.

5 If Sasha and her friends _____ (not / find) the old warehouse, they _____ (not / be) able to set up a gallery.

6 If the gallery _____ (not / have) good reviews, it _____ (probably / not / receive) so many visitors now.

6 Rewrite the sentences so they have a similar meaning. Use second, third and mixed conditionals.

1 She's not an ambitious person. She didn't apply for the job of director.
If she _____ , she _____ .

2 I met my wife, who is German, and now I am living in Germany.
If I _____ , I _____ now.

3 I am not a risk-taker. I am not going to invest my own money in the business.
If I _____ , I _____ .

4 She didn't receive much encouragement. She gave up her plan to become a pilot.
If she _____ , she _____ .

5 I didn't say anything about the situation, because I am not worried about it.
If I _____ , I _____ .

6 He left college and became a ski instructor, and now he's very happy with his life.
If he _____ and _____ , perhaps he _____ with his life.

7 Pronunciation contracted or weak forms

🔊 **63** Listen to these sentences. Are the underlined verbs pronounced as weak forms (W) or are they contracted (C)? Write W or C. Then listen again and repeat.

1 If he asked me, I <u>would</u> certainly offer to help him. _____

2 It <u>would have</u> been easier if you <u>had been</u> there. _____

3 If I <u>had</u> known, I <u>would have</u> told you. _____

4 If he <u>was</u> more thoughtful, he <u>would have</u> remembered your birthday. _____

5 If the meeting <u>were</u> an hour earlier, I <u>would</u> be able to come. _____

Vocabulary *make* and *do*

8 Look at these three expressions used by Sasha when she described her ambition. Choose the correct option to complete the expressions.

1 I knew it would be difficult to *do / make* **a living** from my art.

2 My ambition was to *do / make* **something** within the art world.

3 I *did / made* **odd jobs** like working as a waiter.

9 Complete the sentences. Use the correct form of *make* or *do*.

1 Before you _____ a decision about the career you want, I think you should _____ some research about job opportunities.

2 Thanks for _____ the translation work that I gave you, but I think you've _____ a couple of small mistakes.

3 I've _____ a list of all the things I'd like to _____ when I'm in London.

4 I don't know how he thinks that sitting around all day and _____ nothing will _____ a difference to the result!

8b Wish lists

Reading the forget-it list

1 Read the blog. Choose the statement (a–c) that best summarizes why the author is against making wish lists.

   a It is a selfish thing to do.

   b It won't make you happy.

   c It is unrealistic.

2 Read the blog again. Are the sentences true (T), false (F)? Or is there not enough information (N) to say if the statements are true or false?

   1 John Goddard made his list because he was frightened of dying.

   2 John Goddard's list was full of things that were difficult to achieve.

   3 John Goddard was not able to fulfil all of his wishes.

   4 The author's neighbour was not satisfied with what she had achieved in life.

   5 The author thinks that we choose some things to put on our wish lists because it will win the respect of people we know.

   6 The author regrets that he didn't become a professional musician.

   7 The author can't afford to take a year off to travel.

   8 The author thinks that he could manage to trek across the Himalayas.

The forget-it list

In 1940, a fifteen-year-old American boy decided to make a list of everything he wanted to do in his life. John Goddard, who later became an anthropologist, wrote down 127 goals, most of them very ambitious. They included climbing the world's highest mountains, flying a jet, running a mile in five minutes, reading the whole Encyclopedia Britannica, mastering surfing and visiting the Moon. Amazingly, he managed to do most of them and add several more before he died in 2013. He left behind a book about his adventures, but he also left another legacy – the 'bucket list'. This idea (a list of the things you want to do before you die) was made popular by the 2007 film The *Bucket List*. Now everyone, it seems, has a bucket list, from Bill Clinton to my neighbour who's just celebrated her thirtieth birthday and feels that life is passing her by.

I have some issues with this. For a start, why do you need the excuse of dying to have wishes about what you want to achieve? We're all going to die at some point. Secondly, it becomes rather competitive. Are these really the things that you want to do (for example, become an expert salsa dancer) or are they the things that you would like other people to be impressed by? And lastly, what happens if you fail to achieve some of your goals? You will probably be more full of regret than if you had not made a list in the first place.

So I've come up with an alternative idea: the 'Forget-it list'. This is a list of all the wishes you have that are unlikely to come true and all the things that you might think will make you happier or more fulfilled, but may not be so wonderful after all. For example, I wish I was a professional musician. Forget it – I've got a good job and great colleagues. I wish I could spend a year travelling around South America. Forget it – I've got a family to support – a family I love being with, by the way. I wish I could trek across the Himalayas. Forget it – even though it must be beautiful, it would probably break me physically. What I'm trying to say, in short, is: want what you have and stop wanting what you don't have.

3 Find words or expressions in the blog on page 62 that mean the following.

1 something left for the benefit of future generations (para 1)

2 moving too fast to take advantage of (para 1)

3 a (often poor or false) reason for an action (para 2)

4 another or different (para 3)

5 improbable (para 3)

6 provide money for (para 3)

Grammar *wish* and *if only*

4 Choose the correct verb to complete these wishes.

1 I wish people *stopped / would stop* making bucket lists.

2 I wish I *can / could* take a year off from my work to do the things I want to do.

3 I wish I *travelled / had travelled* more when I was younger.

4 If only I *were / would be* more satisfied with what I have; then I wouldn't need to write a wish list.

5 I wrote a bucket list some years ago, but I wish I *didn't / hadn't*. I feel a lot of pressure because I've only done one of the things on it.

6 I want to go on a cruise, but my partner says they are boring. I wish he *changed / would change* his mind.

7 I bet a lot of people wish John Goddard *didn't start / hadn't started* this trend.

8 My friend said something very funny yesterday. She said 'I wish I *didn't have / wouldn't have* so many regrets.'

5 Complete these wishes. Use the correct form of the verbs in brackets.

1 Oh, no. We're going to be late. I wish we _____ (leave) earlier.

2 I wish you _____ (stop) complaining about the weather. There's nothing I can do about it.

3 I really want to know how Olivia got on at her interview. If only I _____ (have) her number, then I could call her.

4 What would I change about my appearance? Well, I wish I _____ (be) a few centimetres taller, for a start.

5 No one ever listens to my ideas. I wish people _____ (take) me more seriously.

6 I wish the people next door _____ (turn) down that music. I can't concentrate.

6 Pronunciation /s/, /ʃ/ and /tʃ/

🎵 **64** Listen and underline the words that you hear.

1	mass	mash	match
2	sip	ship	chip
3	Sue	shoe	chew
4	Swiss	swish	switch
5	sock	shock	chock
6	bass*	bash	batch

* *bass = a type of fish*

7 Dictation bucket lists

🎵 **65** Listen and complete this opinion of bucket lists.

I am very suspicious of bucket lists now.

They _____ ,

but _____

they have _____ .

In bookshops _____

100 places _____

or *100* _____ .

And if your _____

tiger, there are even _____

where they _____ .

8c A cause for hope?

Listening conservation stories

1 🔘 **66** You are going to hear three people talking about conservation projects. Listen and complete the table.

	What needs to be protected?	Has the conservation work been successful?
1	The mangrove .... in	
2	The West African	
3	The black poplar .... in	

2 🔘 **66** Listen again. Are the sentences true (T) or false (F)? Or is there not enough information (N) to say if the statements are true or false?

1   Every inhabitant of Cancún misses the beautiful mangrove forest.
2   Pollution has badly damaged the coral reef along this part of the coast.
3   In West Africa, conservationists needed to find out where the giraffe went for food.
4   Farmers were killing the giraffes who fed on their land.
5   People associate the word 'conservation' with work in developing countries.
6   The decrease in the numbers of black poplar trees has been quite sudden.

3 🔘 **66** Complete the sentences about the conservation projects using these words. Then listen again and check.

> classic   heroic   rarest   rotting   sale   small
> wonderful   victims

1   Today that forest is buried and .... underneath 500 hotels.
2   This place is a .... example of how not to build a tourist resort.
3   Nature is for .... here.
4   The mangroves are not the only ....
5   A .... effort on the part of conservationists has saved the giraffe.
6   The conservationists could then begin to educate local people about the dangers facing these .... creatures.
7   But in fact, many conservation efforts are .... in scale.
8   The black poplar is one of Britain's .... species of tree.

Cancún   West Africa   Poplar tree

4 Find words and expressions in Exercise 3 that have these meanings:
1   very typical ....
2   a person or thing against which a crime is committed ....
3   placed under the ground ....
4   you can buy it ....
5   decaying or going bad ....

Vocabulary strong feelings

5 Look at these words. Tick (✓) the emotive words.

> back-breaking   criticize   desperate
> interested in   keen on   majestic   tall   tiring

6 Rewrite the text about the black poplar tree. Replace the words in bold with a more emotive word from the box.

> deprived   exploit   giant   most threatened
> over-developed   rescue   wonderful

If you mention the term 'conservation efforts', people often think of attempts to ¹ **save** endangered animals; or to protect ² **poor** communities from ³ **big** corporate organizations who are trying to ⁴ **use** their land. But in fact, many conservation efforts are small in scale and many have ⁵ **good** outcomes. The black poplar tree is one of Britain's ⁶ **rarest** species and its numbers have been declining for decades. That's mainly because much of its natural habitat – the floodplain – has been ⁷ **built on** with new housing.

1   5   ....
2   6   ....
3   7   ....
4   ....

8d Choices

Real life discussing preferences

1 Match the beginnings of the sentences (1–6) with the endings (a–f) to make complete sentences.

1	I prefer walking	a	than cycle.
2	I'd rather walk	b	walked.
3	I like walking	c	if we walked.
4	I'd rather we	d	to cycling.
5	I'd rather	e	not cycle.
6	I think it would be better	f	more than cycling.

2 🎵 **67** Listen to a conversation between friends who are trying to organize a friend's birthday party. Which tasks do they mention?

a buying drinks

b decorating the tent

c doing shopping

d getting hi-fi equipment

e preparing food

f laying tables

3 🎵 **67** Complete the sentences. Then listen to the conversation again and check your answers.

1 I'd _____ any cooking.

2 But if you _____ something else, there are plenty of other things.

3 I don't _____ with the decorations.

4 I could, but I'd rather _____ that.

5 It _____ if I went to get the hi-fi equipment.

6 OK, and I _____ the decorations anyway, so that's perfect.

4 Complete the sentences so they express the same ideas as the sentences in Exercise 3. Use the word in brackets.

1 If I had the choice, I _____ any cooking. (prefer)

2 But if you _____ something else, there are plenty of other things. (rather)

3 I'd _____ with the decorations. (happy)

4 I could, but it _____ if someone else did that. (better)

5 I _____ and get the hi-fi equipment. (rather)

6 I _____ the decorations anyway. (prefer)

5 Pronunciation *do you, would you, shall we*

🎵 **68** Listen and complete the sentences.

1 _____ a proper meal or just something light?

2 _____ a short break?

3 _____ to the film another night?

4 _____ Manchester more than London?

6 Listen and respond talking about preferences

🎵 **69** Listen to someone asking you about your preferences. Respond in your own words. Answer in full sentences and give reasons. Then compare your response with the model answer that follows.

1

> *I'm going to ask you to explain your preferences for certain things. Ready? Here we go: bath or shower?*

> *I prefer having a shower generally. It's quicker and more refreshing.*

8e A wish for change

Writing posting a comment

1 Read the online comment. Answer the questions.

   1   What is the subject of the blog the writer is responding to?

      ....

      ....

   2   Does he agree with the writer of the blog? Why? / Why not?

      ....

      ....

Sean Thompson (Communications specialist)
Thanks for your interesting blog and for drawing attention to this topical issue. I am sure a lot of people will agree with you that people who speak loudly on their phones in public places ought to know better. But I am not convinced that it represents 'anti-social behaviour'.

I was brought up in Brooklyn in New York where people live close together and it wasn't unusual to overhear other people's conversations: discussions, family arguments, jokes. Often it was just their everyday business that you heard: a call to someone to get up, a reminder to buy something from the shops, asking someone to get out of the bathroom. But I don't see this as anti-social; it's social behaviour. Knowing each other's business helps there to be openness between neighbours. Actually, I think it encourages people to talk to each other more.

Of course, some people speak loudly on their phones just to show off. I was on a train recently where a man was loudly discussing a business deal. As if he thought he hadn't impressed the rest of us enough, halfway through the conversation he switched from English into Chinese! But to have laws against speaking loudly in public, as you suggest, is not the answer.

---

2 Writing skills giving vivid examples

a Look at the online comment again. Answer the questions.

   1   What examples support the writer's argument?

      ....

   2   What example(s) show that there are exceptions to his argument?

      ....

b Look at this extract from another comment posted about the same article. Add examples (1–5) to complete the comment.

Great blog. I couldn't agree with you more. People are so inconsiderate in how they use their phones these days: in [1] .... , [2] .... and especially on [3] .... And they always talk about the most boring things like [4] .... and [5] .... As if they think the rest of us are interested!

Word focus *better*

3 Find the phrase with *better* that the writer uses in the comment in Exercise 1. What does the phrase mean (a, b or c)?

   a   have enough sense not to do something
   b   improve on the effort of another person
   c   be more useful or desirable

4 Complete the sentences using these phrases with *better*.

> be better   be better off   go one better
> know better

   1   I'll be in a meeting from 3.00 to 5.00 p.m. so it would .... to send me a text message.

   2   The train companies have put signs up asking people to be considerate when using their phones, but they could .... and ban their use completely.

   3   He's always calling me when I'm busy at work. He should ....

   4   I think we would all .... if the mobile phone had never been invented!

Wordbuilding noun suffixes

1 Write the name of the person who does each of these jobs. Use the correct noun suffix.

1 Someone who works with water pipes and **plumbs** in central heating systems is a _____ .

2 Someone who sells **flowers** or makes flower arrangements is a _____ .

3 Someone who **translates** documents from one language to another is a _____ .

4 Someone who works in the **banking** sector is a _____ .

5 Someone who specializes in preparing medicines in a **pharmacy** is a _____ .

6 Someone who looks after the books in a **library** is a _____ .

7 Someone who prepares the **accounts** for a company is an _____ .

8 Someone who **specializes** in IT problems is a _____ .

9 Someone who does **surgical** operations on people in a hospital is a _____ .

10 Someone who **consults** people about their finances is a financial _____ .

11 Someone who **inspects** tickets on a train is a ticket _____ .

12 Someone who does **optical** tests and makes glasses is an _____ .

2 Underline the general name for a person (male *or* female) with these jobs.

1 someone who sells things: *a salesman / a sales officer / a salesperson*

2 someone who works for the police: *a police operator / a police officer / a police person*

3 someone who works in the fire service: *a fire fighter / a fire manager / a fire person*

4 someone who acts: *an actor / an actress / an acting agent*

5 someone who helps passengers on a plane: *a flight steward / an air hostess / a flight attendant*

Learning skills improving your listening

3 🎧 **70** A key to understanding fast native speech is to understand stress and linking in English pronunciation. Listen to this sentence and note the stress and linking in it.

1 **Stress:** Sorry I just <u>don't</u> <u>accept</u> that.

2 **Linking:** Sorry‿I just don't‿accept that.

4 🎧 **71** Look at these sentences. Underline the stressed syllables and indicate where the sounds are linked. Then listen and check.

1 Globalization helps people in rich countries.

2 They can have goods out of season.

3 But to be honest, I don't need flowers imported from Africa in December.

5 🎧 **72** Read these steps (1–5) for improving your listening skills. Listen again to the third speaker from 8c, Exercise 1 and follow the steps.

1 Write down the words you hear.

2 Read your transcript back. Does it make grammatical sense?

3 Compare your transcript with the audioscript.

4 Note the words and sounds which have the strongest stress. These should be the key words that convey the meaning.

5 Note which words are clearly linked. This will help you to distinguish them the next time you hear them.

Check!

6 Complete the crossword. All the answers are in Student's Book Unit 8.

			1					3	
		2							
		4							
			5						
6					7			8	
						9			
	10								
11									

Across

2 and 6 the name for one of the women who worked as a 'computer' at NASA in the 1950s (6, 4)

5 an animal only found in Madagascar (5)

7 Complete this sentence. If I hadn't missed the bus, I would have _____ on time (4)

9 Complete this sentence: I prefer tea _____ coffee (2)

10 another expression for 'I wish' (2, 4)

11 the superpower most explorers wished they had was to be _____ (9)

Down

1 another word for an aim (4)

3 an aim that is usually an amount or a number (6)

4 what you want to achieve (often in your career) (8)

8 If you create a sound, you 'make a _____ ' (5)

Unit 9 The news

9a Photojournalism

Vocabulary reporting verbs

1 Complete the crossword with reporting verbs

Across

2 Please don't _____ me. I'm doing my best. (British English spelling) (9)

5 I think you've made the wrong choice. I _____ you to think again. (4)

6 I'll only do it if he _____ me to. (4)

7 You always _____ so many questions! (3)

8 I know you took my pen. Don't try to _____ it. (4)

Down

1 I didn't _____ you of breaking the laptop. I just said it was a pity it was broken. (6)

2 My soup is cold. I'm going to _____ to the waiter. (8)

3 The party was a bit noisy, but you didn't need to _____ to call the police! (8)

4 I don't know the best thing to do. What do you _____ ? (7)

Listening re-touching reality

2 🎧 73 Listen to an interview with a journalist talking about altering photos. What two examples do they discuss? Complete the descriptions.

1 The _____ of the February _____ edition of *National Geographic* magazine.

2 A _____ of Nancy Reagan and Raisa Gorbachev in *Picture Week* _____ .

3 🎧 73 Listen again. Are the sentences true (T) or false (F)?

1 Photo editors changed the size of the pyramids in the photo.

2 An editor said that the changes to the photo were OK because it was a cover photo.

3 He also said that technology had made altering images more acceptable.

4 Editors have said that it's acceptable to alter covers because they advertise the book or magazine.

5 The photographer thinks that there's no difference between manipulating cover images and altering news photos.

6 *Picture Week* changed two photos to suggest the people in them had friendly faces.

7 People thought that the *Picture Week* photo was unacceptable.

8 People are not able to distinguish between reality and fiction.

Glossary
alter (v) /ˈɒltə/ change
digitally enhanced (adj) /ˈdɪdʒɪt(ə)li ɪnˈhɑːnst/ improved using digital technology
manipulate (v) /məˈnɪpjʊleɪt/ to digitally change information or images (on a computer)
touch up (v) /tʌtʃ ˈʌp/ make small changes to improve an image

4 Pronunciation long vowel /əʊ/

🔊 **74** Listen to these words. Pay attention to the long /əʊ/ sound. Then listen again and repeat.

boat   don't   fellow   going   growing   hotel
know   local   opposed   own   photo   sofa

Grammar verb patterns with reporting verbs

5 Rewrite these sentences using the reporting verbs given.

1 People said that the magazine had manipulated reality.
   People **accused** the magazine _____

2 The editor said they had altered the image.
   The editor **admitted** _____

3 But he said they hadn't done anything wrong.
   But he **denied** _____

4 He said modern technology made it easy to alter images.
   He **blamed** _____

5 Some editors tell their designers that it is OK to alter images for covers.
   Some editors **persuade** _____

6 People weren't happy and said that they had been given a false impression.
   People **complained** _____

7 Some people say, 'Don't trust a photo if there's anything important depending on it.'
   Some people **warn** you _____

6 Complete the text using the correct form of the verbs. Use prepositions where necessary.

In the past, people criticized photographers ¹_____ (invade) people's privacy or ²_____ (take) pictures that did not reflect the reality of a situation. But nowadays, in the age of digital photography, there is a new problem. How do we know that the photo has not been altered after it has been taken? It would be wrong to blame the photographer ³_____ (manipulate) some of the photos that appear in our newspapers and magazines. A photo editor might be asked ⁴_____ (alter) a photo digitally in order to make a good story. For example, someone might suggest ⁵_____ (use) Photoshop to make a film star's face look more attractive. Or they might urge the photo editor ⁶_____ (add) an image of a frightened child into a photo of a street protest. You can perhaps forgive the editor ⁷_____ (make) the first alteration, but what about the second? That is a practice people should possibly refuse ⁸_____ (accept).

7 Dictation digital photography

🔊 **75** Listen to someone talking about analogue and digital cameras. Then complete the text.

1 Like many of his fellow professionals, photographer Fritz Hoffman _____ .

2 A digital camera _____ , but an analogue camera _____ .

3 Hoffman also claims _____ .

4 That's so that _____ .

9b News in brief

Reading good-news stories

1 Read the four newspaper stories. Match the headlines (a–d) with the stories (1–4).

   a Better to give than receive
   b A sense of community
   c A charmed life
   d An old secret

2 Write the number of the story (1–4) next to the statements (a–f).

This story shows that:
   a you can help people without spending a lot of money. ....
   b there is not one right way to do something.
   ....
   c you can inspire other people by your actions.
   ....
   d people are born lucky. ....
   e there is a good and a bad side to every situation. ....
   f people's faith in human nature can be restored.
   ....

News in brief

1 ....

In the UK street riots of 2011, it is estimated that rioters caused over £100 million of damage to their own communities. But for every negative, there's often a positive, as the case of Mr Biber, a London barber, shows. Mr Biber's barber shop in London, where he has been cutting hair for forty years, was among those damaged, and the 89-year-old thought he had lost everything. But word got around and a website to support him was set up. Donations raised £35,000, enough to make the necessary repairs. Moreover, people's generosity gave Mr Biber the encouragement to carry on doing what he loves.

2 ....

Some people believe that the secret to a long life is a glass of red wine every day. For others, it is plenty of exercise. But few people would claim that eating fast food helps. They obviously haven't met 100-year old Catherine Reddoch from Matamata, New Zealand. Every day, using her zimmer frame to support her, she walks a kilometre – a journey which takes her one hour – to her local hamburger café. Here she eats a cheeseburger and drinks a cup of hot chocolate. Mrs Reddoch is not concerned about the fat content of the meal. 'I eat anything and everything – I like my cheeseburgers,' she says. The café owner was reported to have put a plaque with Catherine's name on it on her usual seat to celebrate her hundredth birthday.

3 ....

Secret Agent L is the brainchild of one woman, Laura Miller. Laura's mission is to spread kindness in the world. She does this by doing small acts of kindness, like leaving a flower on someone's car windscreen or making a nice walking stick for someone to find when they are on a long walk.

The idea is that when someone finds these secret gifts, it brightens up their day. It is believed that Secret Agent L now has over 1,800 followers around the world, all creating and sharing their ideas for similar kind acts.

4 ....

A 21-year-old man who drove his car over the edge of the Grand Canyon escaped with only a few minor injuries. Witnesses said that his car had plunged two hundred feet into the mile-deep canyon before hitting a tree which stopped it falling further. He is not thought to have been speeding, but the exact cause of the accident remains unknown. Another visitor found him lying in the road after he had apparently climbed back out of the canyon. The emergency services said he was an extremely lucky man.

Glossary
plaque (n) /plæk/ a small metal sign
riot (n) /ˈraɪət/ a violent protest

3 Find words in the stories on page 70 that mean:
1 gifts of money (story 1) _____
2 a walking aid for old people (story 2)
   _____
3 an original idea (story 3) _____
4 make more cheerful (story 3) _____
5 fell or dived (story 4) _____
6 driving too fast (story 4) _____

Grammar passive reporting verbs

4 Underline an example of a passive reporting verb in each story on page 70.

> ▶ **TENSES IN PASSIVE REPORTING VERBS**
>
> Note how these tenses are transformed from active to passive.
>
> | *Active* | *Passive* |
> | --- | --- |
> | People say that | It is said that |
> | | (She) is said + to + infinitive |
> | People have said that | It has been said that |
> | People said that | It was said that |
> | | (She) was said + to + infinitive / perfect infinitive |
> | People used to say that | It used to be said that |

5 Look at the grammar box. Rewrite the underlined phrases using passive reporting verbs.
1 <u>People say that</u> the summers are very hot.
   It is said that the summers are very hot.
2 Everyone <u>knows</u> that reading is important.
   Reading _____ to be important.
3 People <u>used to believe</u> that the Earth was flat.
   It _____ that the Earth was flat.
4 People <u>have estimated</u> that the bridge will cost $10 million.
   It _____ that the bridge will cost $10 million.
5 People <u>thought</u> that she was missing.
   She _____ to be missing.
6 People <u>said</u> that she regretted her actions.
   She _____ to have regretted her actions.

6 Rewrite the sentences using passive reporting verbs.
1 People say that there is always a positive side to things.
   It is said that there is always a positive side to things.
2 People hoped that the secret gifts would brighten up someone's day.
   It _____ the secret gifts would brighten up someone's day.
3 People used to think that a glass of red wine was good for you.
   It _____ a glass of red wine was good for you.

4 Most people don't recommend eating fast food if you want to live longer.
   Eating fast food _____ if you want to live longer.
5 People expect Mr Biber to carry on working.
   It _____ Mr Biber _____ working.
6 People said that the tree had prevented the car from falling further.
   The tree _____ the car from falling further.
7 People considered the man was very lucky.
   The man _____ very lucky.
8 People have reported great success with the new app.
   It _____ the new app has been very successful.

Vocabulary positive adjectives

7 Put the letters in the correct order to make adjectives describing good-news stories.
1 marching _____
2 usaming _____
3 springini _____
4 aggening _____
5 shiningsato _____
6 potisimtic _____

8 Match the adjectives in Exercise 7 with these adjectives (a–e) with a similar meaning.
a giving hope _____
b funny _____
c amazing _____
d attractive _____ , _____
e giving inspiration _____

9 Pronunciation weak forms in verbs

🔊 **76** Listen to the auxiliary verbs in these sentences. Note how they are pronounced using the weak form. Then listen again and repeat.
1 It was estimated that £100 million worth of damage was caused in the riots.
2 It is believed that Secret Agent L has more than 200 followers.
3 It was thought that the driver had fallen asleep at the wheel of his car.
4 It was expected that the injured man would make a full recovery.
5 It has been estimated that fifty per cent of the population will be overweight by 2020.
6 It had been thought that diet was more important than exercise.

9c Fairness in reporting

Listening balanced reporting

1 🎵 **77** Listen to a journalist talking about balanced reporting. Which statement (a–c) best summarizes the journalist's argument?

a Broadcasters and news writers often just want to present their own view.

b It is often a mistake for broadcasters and news writers to try to present both sides of an argument equally.

c It is very important for broadcasters and news writers to present both sides of an argument equally.

2 🎵 **77** Listen to the report again. Choose the correct option to complete the sentences.

1 Broadcasters and news writers don't want to be seen as being in favour of *a particular / the stronger* side.

2 A radio story about climate change usually has interviews with *one expert / two experts*.

3 Most of the scientific evidence supports the view that global warming has *natural / man-made* causes.

4 In the 1970s debate about whether smoking was harmful to health, broadcasters usually represented *only one view / both views*.

5 Scientists who denied the link between smoking and disease were often *working for tobacco companies / not real scientists*.

6 People say that the amount of time given to each view should be in relation to the *number of supporters / amount of real evidence* on each side.

3 Look at the audioscript on page 124 and find words that mean:

1 showing favour to one side (adjective, para 1)

2 basic (adjective, para 2)

3 very great or strong (adjective, para 2)

4 gives a false impression of (verb, para 4)

5 properly corresponding in size (adjective, para 4)

Word focus *word*

4 Look at these expressions with *word* and choose the correct definition (a or b).

1 **From the word go,** the restaurant was full every night.
   a from when we had permission
   b from the start

2 Jamie has been behaving very strangely recently. Can you **have a quiet word with** him?
   a be very strict with   b talk privately to

3 Please **don't say a word** to Tabitha about the cup I broke. It's her favourite.
   a don't mention   b lie

4 He said I would never be successful as a professional artist but he had to **eat his words**.
   a admit he was wrong   b apologize

5 Complete the sentences using the expressions with *word*.

don't take my word for it	one person's word
eat my words	against another's
from the word go	was lost for words
gave his word	word of mouth
have the last word	

1 We get most of our new customers by _____. We don't really advertise.

2 I said that there was no way he could win the singing competition. I may have to _____ !

3 It is just _____. In the end, you'll just have to decide who you believe.

4 If you don't believe me, then _____. Check the facts for yourself.

5 He _____ that he would not tell anyone my secret.

6 It's been a great company to work for. _____, my boss really supported me.

7 I didn't know what to say – I _____.

8 She's very argumentative and always has to _____.

9d Spreading the news

Real life reporting what you have heard

1 Complete the sentences. Use a verb in each space. Do the sentences express belief (B) or disbelief (D)?

		B	D
1	I wouldn't _____ her word for it.	☐	☐
2	She generally _____ her facts right.	☐	☐
3	I can well _____ it.	☐	☐
4	He tends to _____ things.	☐	☐
5	That doesn't _____ me.	☐	☐
6	I'd _____ that with a pinch of salt.	☐	☐

2 🎧 **78** Listen to a conversation between two friends, Jane and Annie, and answer the questions.

1 What is the news about Patrick that Jane wants to share?

_____

_____

2 Who did she hear this news from?

_____

3 What does Annie ask Jane to do with the news?

_____

_____

3 🎧 **78** Complete the sentences from the conversation. Then listen again and check.

> *verbs*: heard   reckons   seems
> *prepositions*: about   to
> *adverbs*: apparently   supposedly
> *nouns*: gossip   pinch

1 Did you hear the good news _____ (*preposition*) Patrick?

2 Well, _____ (*adverb*) he was spotted by someone from a big theatrical agency.

3 She _____ (*verb*) that it won't be long before we see him on TV.

4 Well, I'd take that with a _____ (*noun*) of salt if I were you.

5 No, according _____ (*preposition*) Kate, it's more than that.

6 Well, that'd be fantastic. I _____ (*verb*) that it was really difficult to get that kind of work.

7 Don't worry. I'm not the type to spread _____ (*noun*). Does the agency take a big fee?

8 It _____ (*verb*) that they only take ten or fifteen per cent, _____ (*adverb*).

4 Pronunciation the schwa

🎧 **79** Listen to these words from the conversation. Underline the stressed syllable and circle the schwa / ə / sounds.
Example: supposedly

1	comedy	5	according
2	festival	6	difficult
3	apparently	7	agency
4	reckon	8	theatrical

5 Listen and respond reporting what you have heard

🎧 **80** Listen to someone giving you some news about government taxes. Respond after the tone with your own words. Then compare your response with the model answer that follows.

1

> *Did you hear the good news about taxes?*

> *Good news about taxes? No, what happened?*

9e News story

A

Bama has a higher proportion of people over 100 years old than anywhere else in China. The exact reason for this is not known. Some say it is the mountain air, others that strong magnetic fields help sleep. ¹ _____ ,
it has attracted a lot of tourists who want to benefit from its healthy environment.
² _____ the tourists increase traffic pollution and also leave their rubbish behind.
³ _____ , the local population who before lived on simple locally grown food, are now eating the less healthy, processed food that the tourism has brought with it.

B

⁴ _____ a new eco-resort that is now being built will help to reduce this pollution and preserve the old Bama.

C

Bama in Guangxi Province is a quiet Chinese village with a reputation for well-being and long life. Because of this, it has recently become a popular destination for Chinese 'health' tourists.
⁵ _____ , with so many people visiting to escape the pollution in Chinese cities, the features that make Bama special are themselves in danger.

D

'It's a paradox,' says one local man, aged 84. 'In one way the tourists bring money and jobs for us, but ⁶ _____ , they bring pollution.'

Writing a news article

1 Read the news story. Put the paragraphs (A–D) in the correct order.

1 _____ 2 _____ 3 _____ 4 _____

2 Look at the news story again. Which paragraph:

1 gives the key information? _____
2 gives the details? _____
3 gives a comment on the situation? _____
4 offers a solution? _____

3 Complete the news story with these phrases.

at the same time	The problem is that
But now	What is more
It is hoped that	Whatever the reason

4 Writing skill using quotations

Complete these quotations. Add quotation marks and other punctuation where necessary.

1 One resident described his life in Bama. I have everything I want here he said. I can go fishing when I want to. I don't have any stress. And then he added why would I want to go and live in the city?

2 Some people come here to take wedding photos said another resident which is fine. But when they leave their rubbish behind, I get very angry.

3 A health tourist said before I came here I could hardly breathe or speak, because the pollution in my city was so bad. Now I sing every day he said with a big smile on his face.

Wordbuilding forming adjectives from verbs

1 Complete the sentences using the verbs + -ing.

> charm   confuse   depress   inspire
> refresh   tire   touch   worry

1 It is _____ that she is so late – she's normally very punctual.
2 The news story was rather _____ . You couldn't work out why the daughter had left her family.
3 It's very _____ to hear a story about a business which doesn't just do things to make money. You don't often hear that.
4 He is a really _____ man – polite, interesting and kind.
5 The story about two friends overcoming their difficulties was very _____ .
6 Environmental news is often _____ , but in this case the story offered hope.
7 The news featured the _____ story of a fourteen-year-old girl who got a part-time job to help support her family.
8 It's very _____ to follow a film with subtitles for three hours.

2 Make adjectives using verbs + -ive.

1 good at **inventing** _inventive_ (from _invent_)
2 good at **persuading** _____
3 good at **creating** _____
4 liking to **compete** _____
5 **producing** a lot _____
6 **talking** a lot _____
7 wanting to **protect** _____
8 **attracting** you _____

Learning skills keeping a learning diary

3 What is a learning diary and why is it a good idea to keep one? Look at these reasons and compare them with your own ideas.

> • To learn from your mistakes and your successes
>
> • To track your progress
>
> • To make clear targets for the next stage of your learning
>
> • To record what you have learned

4 Read the following actions which can help you to evaluate and personalize your learning.

Actions

1 Write down your experiences of learning after each lesson: what you found easy, what you found difficult, what the most important thing you learned was.

2 Note down mistakes that you have made before.

3 Make a note of an extract, even a sentence, that you particularly liked and try to memorize it.

4 Set yourself a small task based on the language you learned in your last lesson, e.g. describe a good news story, report what someone said to you, or describe a situation where somebody's reputation was questioned.

5 Apply the actions (1–4) for Unit 9. Then remember to do it for your next lesson!

Check!

6 Do the quiz. You can find all the answers in Student's Book Unit 9.

Quiz Time

1 Add one more reporting verb that is followed by each of these patterns.
  a verb + *to* + infinitive: *promise, threaten,* _____
  b verb + someone + *to* + infinitive: *ask, encourage,* _____
  c verb + someone/something + preposition + -ing: *criticize, thank,* _____

2 Complete these sentences about the characters in Unit 9.
  a Sharbat Gula's photo is one of the most i_____ images of our time.
  b Dr Zhavoronkov is trying to find drugs that will slow down the a_____ process.
  c The pilot Peter Burkill went from hero to z_____ .

3 Complete the phrases about the news.
  a The best form of advertising is when news travels by word of m_____ .
  b News reports often like to end with a g_____-news story.
  c It's not a good thing to g_____ about people behind their backs.
  d You can usually tell what a story is going to be about by looking at the h_____ .

Unit 10 Talented people

10a The great communicator

Listening

1 🔊 **81** Read the questions. Then listen to the description of Ronald Reagan and complete the answers.

1 Where was Ronald Reagan raised?
  In a ....

2 What jobs did he have before he entered politics?
  He worked as a ....
  and ....

3 What important historical event occurred during his presidency?
  The collapse of ....

4 What did people who criticized him say about his speeches?
  They said he could only ....

5 What made him a great communicator?
  His ability to ....

6 What other factor worked in his favour as president?
  It was a time of ....

2 🔊 **81** Look at the words and phrases in bold from the description of Ronald Reagan. Choose the correct meaning (a or b). Then listen again and check.

1 His skills as **an orator** were noticed and he was persuaded to run for Governor of California.
  a a politician
  b a public speaker

2 He was often ridiculed for not being very clever – a **second-rate** actor …
  a not very good
  b slow-speaking

3 Reagan always **gave the impression** that he was listening …
  a made others believe
  b wanted others to think

4 He made people feel that they **mattered**.
  a were lucky
  b were important

5 The economy **thrived** during his presidency.
  a did badly
  b did well

6 Reagan's style of communication **stands out**.
  a is noticeable
  b is old-fashioned

Vocabulary careers

3 🔊 **81** Complete the sentences with the correct verb. Then listen again to the description and check your answers.

1 Ronald Reagan .... from Eureka College, Illinois with a degree in economics and sociology.

2 He .... for a short time as a radio broadcaster in Iowa.

3 He moved to Los Angeles to .... a career as an actor in films and television.

4 After .... the Republican Party in 1962, his skills as an orator were noticed.

5 He .... a good job as Governor of California.

6 He went on to .... the President of the United States between 1981 and 1989.

Grammar articles: *a(n)*, *the* or zero article?

4 Complete with *the* or zero article (–).

Countries:	.... Japan, ... United Arab Emirates, ... Netherlands, ... Thailand
Places:	.... Amazon River, ... countryside, ... Moon, ... Mount Everest
Times:	.... weekend, ... Saturday, ... April, ... spring
Other:	.... breakfast, ... police, ... poor, ... biology

5 Complete the sentences with *a(n), the* or zero article (–).

1 After joining _____ Republican Party in 1962, Reagan's skills as an orator were noticed.

2 Reagan was President of _____ United States between 1981 and 1989.

3 He remains one of _____ most popular American presidents of _____ past fifty years.

4 Ronald Reagan understood that it is important to be _____ good communicator.

5 When he was speaking to you, Reagan always gave _____ impression that he was listening too.

6 He looked _____ people in _____ eye, smiled at them and made them feel special.

7 He presided over a time of _____ great economic growth in _____ America.

8 _____ things weren't great for _____ most Americans and he gave them _____ hope.

9 It obviously helped that _____ US economy thrived during _____ time that he was President.

10 If you can connect with _____ ordinary people, there's very little you can do wrong.

6 Pronunciation linking vowels

a 🎵 **82** Listen to these phrases. What sound links the words: /w/, /j/ or /r/?

	/w/	/j/	/r/
1 one idea‿at a time			
2 he‿often spoke to ordinary people			
3 do‿a good job			
4 the beginning of the‿end			
5 an area‿of outstanding beauty			
6 China‿and India			
7 look someone in the‿eye			
8 too‿expensive			
9 it's so‿exciting			

b 🎵 **82** Listen again and check. Then practise saying each phrase.

7 Dictation careers

🎵 **83** Listen to three people describing their careers. Write down the words you hear. Be careful – many of the sentences contain the linking sounds /w/, /j/ or /r/.

1 I guess I _____

2 It's not easy _____

3 I was always told _____

Vocabulary qualifications

8 Complete the job interview between an interviewer (I) and an applicant (A) using these words.

background	experience	knowledge
qualifications	qualities	talents

I: So can you tell me first a little bit about your
1 _____ ?

A: Sure. My mother's French and my father's English. I was brought up in France and …

I: And do you have any previous
2 _____ of journalism?

A: Yes. At university I was editor of the student magazine and after that I worked for a local radio station …

I: What 3 _____ do you have?

A: I have a degree in media studies and a diploma in …

I: What would you say are your best
4 _____ ?

A: I'm a very organized person, I'm hard-working and I think I …

I: Do you have any 5 _____ of European politics?

A: Well, I read the papers regularly and I take a great interest in current affairs …

I: And lastly. Do you have any particular
6 _____ ? Things that might make you different from other candidates?

A: I'm good at learning languages and I'm a good photographer.

10b An inspirational scientist

Reading

1 Read the article quickly and underline the part of the text that answers these questions.
1 What is the aim of Hayat Sindi's work?
2 What is the problem with medicines used to fight diseases like hepatitis?
3 What is the tool that can help with this?
4 Why did Sindi move to England?
5 What is her hope for other women like her?

2 Read the article again and answer the questions. Choose the correct option (a–c).
1 Which of the following is NOT a quality of the new tool?
  a small   b powerful   c high-tech
2 Where is more health monitoring needed?
  a in developed countries
  b in developing countries
  c everywhere
3 Compared to results from a medical laboratory, this tool's results are:
  a more accurate.   b more positive.
  c quicker.
4 Sindi's family was not:
  a rich.   b academic.   c traditional.
5 Sindi studied hard in England because she was afraid of:
  a her parents.   b failure.   c feeling lonely.
6 Sindi would like women to use their education to:
  a go abroad.
  b help their own countries.
  c become scientists.

3 Find these words and phrases in the article. Choose the best definition (a–c).
1 entire (para 1)
  a complete   b modern   c sophisticated
2 detect (para 2)
  a have   b find   c solve
3 low-tech (para 2)
  a cheap   b small   c not sophisticated
4 let (her family) down (para 3)
  a return back to   b disappoint
  c personal
5 overcoming the obstacles (para 3)
  a ignoring the problems
  b doing better than expected
  c dealing with difficulties successfully
6 guidance (para 4)
  a teaching   b comfort   c advice

Something the size of a postage stamp, which costs just a penny apiece, could be a medical breakthrough that will save millions of lives. According to biotechnology scientist Hayat Sindi, this tiny piece of paper has the same power as an entire medical laboratory. 'My mission is to find simple, inexpensive ways to monitor health,' Sindi says. She believes that new technology created by a team at Harvard University will make it possible, and she co-founded the charity 'Diagnostics For All' to produce and distribute the innovation.

In the developing world, powerful drugs are used to fight diseases like HIV/AIDS, tuberculosis and hepatitis. But these medicines can cause liver damage. In developed countries, doctors monitor patients' progress and change the medication if they detect problems. But in isolated, rural corners of the world, no one monitors patients to see what is working and what isn't. The tragic result is that millions are dying from the same drugs that are supposed to cure them. The small piece of paper is a low-tech tool which detects disease by analysing bodily fluids. Positive results, which show up in less than a minute, are indicated by a change in colour on the paper.

Sindi's determination to solve challenging problems does not surprise people who know her. Despite coming from a poor background, never travelling outside Saudi Arabia or speaking a word of English, she moved to England to attend university. Alone, homesick, and worried that she would fail and let her family down, she prepared for her college entrance exams, for which she studied for up to twenty hours a day. (She had learned English by watching the BBC news.) Overcoming the obstacles, she got into Cambridge University and became the first Saudi woman to study biotechnology there. She went on to get a PhD and become a visiting scholar at Harvard University.

Sindi's passion and achievements have made her an inspiration to young women across the Middle East. 'I want all women to believe in themselves and know they can transform society. When I speak in schools, the first thing I ask the children attending is to draw a picture of a scientist. 99.9% of them draw an old bald man with glasses. When I tell them I'm a scientist, they look so surprised.' A new foundation she has launched gives guidance and money to encourage young women who attend university abroad to bring their skills back to their homelands.

Grammar relative clauses

4 Read the article on page 78 and find examples of the following.

1 two defining relative clauses using *that* (paras 1 and 2)

2 a defining relative clause using *which* (para 2)

3 a defining relative clause using *who* (para 3)

4 a defining relative clause with no relative pronoun (para 4)

5 a non-defining relative clause using *which* (para 2)

6 a non-defining relative clause that uses a preposition (para 3)

7 *what* used as a relative pronoun (para 2)

5 Complete the sentences with the correct relative pronouns. Sometimes no pronoun is necessary and sometimes you will need to add a preposition.

1 This is the part of the laboratory .... we test new drugs.

2 Harvard University, ... was founded in 1636, is the oldest university in the USA.

3 The lecturers, ... come from all over the world, are highly respected scientists.

4 I think .... Sindi did in moving to a strange country was very brave.

5 The best teacher .... I ever had was a woman named Sally Howkins.

6 Biotechnology is the only course .... I was really interested in.

7 There aren't many people .... I disagree strongly, but Tom is definitely one.

8 It's a university .... reputation has grown enormously in the last ten years.

6 Write sentences using relative clauses. Use the correct relative pronouns and use commas where necessary.

1 The piece of paper is the size of a postage stamp. It could save thousands of lives.

2 The charity 'Diagnostics for All' produces the tool. It was co-founded by Sindi.

3 The tool will be used in developing countries. It is difficult to find clinics there.

4 People say things about existing drugs. I agree with the things they say.

5 The results show up on the paper. The paper's colour changes if there is a problem.

6 Sindi went to England. She was a young woman at the time.

7 Sindi later went to Harvard. She was the first Saudi woman to study biotechnology at Cambridge University.

8 Sindi has become an inspiration for other women. They want to follow her example.

7 Grammar extra reduced relative clauses

> ▶ GRAMMAR EXTRA reduced relative clauses
>
> We sometimes use a participle in place of a relative clause.
>
> **Present participle**   *doing*
> She works in Oxford, ~~where she does~~ research. (active)
>
> **Past participle**   *studied*
> It's a subject ~~which is studied~~ by very few people. (passive)
> Notice that we can't use a reduced relative cause when the relative pronoun is the object of the relative clause.

Look at the grammar box. Rewrite these sentences with (full) relative clauses.

1 She believes that new technology <u>created</u> at Harvard University will make it possible.

2 The first thing I ask the children <u>attending</u> the class is to draw a picture of a scientist.

8 Replace the underlined relative clauses in these sentences with reduced relative clauses.

1 Sindi's low-tech tool helps people <u>who are suffering</u> from the negative effects of the drugs.

2 People <u>who live</u> far away from hospitals and clinics will benefit from this technology.

3 The same medicines, <u>which have been designed</u> to fight disease, can also harm people.

4 Sindi, <u>who was determined</u> to succeed, studied up to twenty hours a day.

5 A new foundation, <u>which was launched</u> recently by Sindi, offers help to young women <u>who want</u> to follow a career in science.

10c Harriet Tubman

Listening

1 🔊 **84** Check you understand the meaning of these words. Then listen to a description of the life of Harriet Tubman. Tick (✓) the things she was.

☐ a politician   ☐ an army officer
☐ an anti-slavery campaigner   ☐ a farmer
☐ a spy   ☐ a mother
☐ a train driver   ☐ a writer
☐ a nurse   ☐ a public speaker

2 🔊 **84** Listen to the description again and choose the best option (a–c) to complete each statement.

1 Harriet Tubman's face has recently started to appear:
  a   outside the USA.
  b   on a US bank note.
  c   next to that of Andrew Jackson.

2 Harriet's disability affected her ability to:
  a   concentrate.
  b   stay awake.
  c   stand upright.

3 Arriving in a free state was:
  a   a painful moment.
  b   a confusing moment.
  c   a beautiful moment.

4 Harriet worked on the 'Underground Railroad' as a:
  a   guide to other slaves trying to escape.
  b   guard against people who wanted to stop slaves escaping.
  c   keeper of a safe house where slaves could hide.

5 Black people were good spies because most white southerners didn't think:
  a   black people were interested in the war.
  b   black people were clever enough to be spies.
  c   the northern states were using spies.

6 Tubman did not receive an honour from the government for her military service until:
  a   she retired.
  b   she married a second time.
  c   she died.

3 Look at the underlined words from the description of Harriet Tubman's life. Explain the meaning in your own words.

1 to escape to a <u>neighbouring</u> 'free' state

2 'I felt I was in <u>heaven</u>'

3 She was a <u>determined</u> woman

4 she had to survive on her husband's <u>pension</u>

5 campaigning for <u>voting rights</u> for women

4 Pronunciation word stress in adjectives ending -ive

a 🔊 **85** Listen to the adjectives ending in -ive. Underline the stressed syllable in each word.

1 effective   5 persuasive
2 impressive   6 sensitive
3 supportive   7 decisive
4 positive   8 talkative

b What is the rule for words that end with vowel + -tive? What is the rule for the other words?

Word focus *self*

5 Complete the expressions with *self*. The first letter is given for you.

1 I felt very self-c_____ and nervous standing up there in front of 200 people.

2 She showed a lot of self-c_____ in not losing her temper. I'm sure I would have been very angry.

3 I'm afraid most people vote for what is in their own self-i_____ rather than in the public interest.

4 My sister is a self-m_____ woman. She set up her business all by herself.

5 Self-h_____ books can be very useful if you are looking for ways to change your life.

6 We try to teach children to be self-c_____ and to believe in their own abilities.

10d The right job

Real life describing skills, talents and experience

1 Complete these expressions using the correct preposition.

1 At university, I specialized _____ photojournalism.
2 I'm very familiar _____ your magazine.
3 I'm good _____ spotting an interesting story.
4 I have some experience _____ news photography.
5 I think I'd be suited _____ working in this kind of environment.
6 I feel quite comfortable _____ tight deadlines.
7 I'm very keen _____ the idea of working closely with other journalists.
8 I'm serious _____ wanting to become a full-time news photographer.

2 🎧 **86** Listen to three people describing their skills at a job interview. What job are they applying for?

_____

_____

3 🎧 **86** Listen again and answer the questions about each of the applicants.

1 What are the skills or talents of each applicant?
Applicant 1

_____

_____

Applicant 2

_____

_____

Applicant 3

_____

_____

2 What does each speaker lack experience of?
Applicant 1

_____

_____

Applicant 2

_____

_____

Applicant 3

_____

_____

4 Grammar extra adjective + *-ing* or *to* + infinitive

> ▶ **ADJECTIVE + *-ING* or *TO* + INFINITIVE**
>
> Some adjectives can be followed by a preposition + *-ing* or by an infinitive.
>
> *I'm interested **in learning** French.*
> *I'm happy **to show** you how it works.*

Look at the grammar box. Complete the sentences. Use the correct form of the verb: *-ing* form or *to* + infinitive.

1 I'd be keen on _____ (participate) in one of your trial days.
2 I'll be sad _____ (leave) this place.
3 I'm interested in _____ (travel) to new places.
4 I'm excited about _____ (do) field research in India.
5 I'm very keen _____ (work) abroad.
6 I'd be interested _____ (find out) more about the job.

5 Pronunciation difficult words

🎧 **87** Practise saying these pairs of words. Then listen and check your pronunciation.

1 although   also
2 clothes   cloth
3 private   privacy
4 knowledge   know-how
5 suit   sweet
6 island   Iceland
7 receipt   recipe
8 thorough   through

6 Listen and respond describing skills, talents and experience

🎧 **88** Listen to questions at an interview for a job as a journalist with a local newspaper. Respond with your own words. Then compare your response with the model answer that follows.

1
So what did you study at university?

I studied media, but I specialized in newspaper journalism.

10e First impressions

Writing a personal profile

1 Read the personal profiles below. Which profile is written by someone who:

a wants to do voluntary work? ....
b is renting out a room? ....
c is looking for their first job? ....
d is an experienced professional? ....

1

I'm a young musician and song-writer living in East Nashville, Tennessee. I live in a beautiful house [1] <u>with</u> a large spare room. I'm a friendly person [2] <u>who is very interested in</u> other cultures and I really enjoy having guests to stay from other parts of the world.

2

I am a recent graduate from Manchester University [3] <u>whose ambition is to work</u> in the sports and leisure industry. I am a hard-working person [4] <u>with a passion for</u> sport and healthy living. I am ready to work in any junior position – administrative or operational – so that I can build up my practical knowledge of this industry.

3

An IT consultant [5] <u>with specialist knowledge of</u> financial software, I am a flexible individual [6] <u>who is experienced in</u> advising both large and small companies.

4

I am an enthusiastic (but administratively overloaded!) teacher looking for an opportunity to travel abroad and use my skills to help children [7] <u>who have limited access</u> to education. I am a creative individual [8] <u>with a love of teaching</u> younger children (4 to 7-year-olds) using games and physical activities.

---

2 Writing skill using *with*

Look at the profiles again. Rewrite the underlined relative clauses using *with*, and the *with*-phrases using relative clauses.

1 ....
2 ....
3 ....
4 ....
5 ....
6 ....
7 ....
8 ....

Vocabulary personal qualities

3 Match the adjectives (1–6) describing personal qualities in list A with adjectives (a–f) with a similar meaning in list B.

A	**B**
1 easy-going	a intelligent
2 passionate	b imaginative
3 adaptable	c relaxed
4 creative	d (very) interested
5 bright	e flexible
6 curious	f very enthusiastic

4 Complete this personal profile by writing one word in each space.

I am a young, [1] .... website designer [2] .... six years industry experience who [3] .... in creating websites that use video and special effects. I think that most websites aren't very dynamic and my [4] .... is to create websites [5] .... are more fun and exciting to use.
I have many good recommendations from customers and you [6] .... see some of the websites I [7] .... created by clicking on the links below.

Wordbuilding verb (+ preposition) + noun collocations

1 In each of these groups, one of the verbs does NOT collocate with the noun on the right. Put a line through this verb.

1	follow / do / have	a career
2	make / do / attend	a course
3	acquire / learn / get	a skill
4	take / make / pass	an exam
5	get / win / acquire	promotion
6	gain / win / get	experience
7	possess / own / develop	a talent
8	do / work / get	a job
9	gain / earn / get	a qualification
10	join / set up / take on	a company

2 Complete the description of someone's career using verbs from Exercise 1. You will need to use the correct form of the verb.

When I was nineteen I ¹ _____ an exam to get into a drama school in London, but I was unsuccessful. At that point, I had to decide whether to try to ² _____ a career in acting or just abandon the idea and ³ _____ a completely different kind of job. All my friends told me that I ⁴ _____ a natural talent for acting and that I didn't need to ⁵ _____ a qualification to prove it. So instead, I ⁶ _____ a small theatre company and ⁷ _____ experience of acting that way. Just by working with other actors I was able to ⁸ _____ new skills and two years ago I was asked by the National Theatre to perform in a production of Shakespeare's *The Tempest*. I have never looked back!

Learning skills the language of learning

3 When you learn a language, you often need to ask questions about it. Look at the terms (1–8). Then match the terms with the definitions (a–h).

1 a part of speech
2 past participle
3 a colloquial expression
4 an idiom
5 a false friend
6 a collocation
7 register
8 a euphemism

a two words that naturally go together
b a phrase whose meaning is not clear from the individual words it is composed of
c the level of formality
d e.g. noun, verb, adjective, adverb, preposition
e a word that looks similar in two languages but has different meanings
f the third form of the verb, e.g. 'go, went, <u>gone</u>'
g a word or phrase that expresses an idea more politely or gently
h a phrase used in everyday informal speech

4 Answer these questions about words from Unit 9.

1 What is the past participle of *feel*? _____
2 What part of speech is *the*? _____
3 What verb collocates with *knowledge*?

_____

4 Is *grab someone's attention* an idiom? _____
5 What register are the personal profiles on page 82 of the Workbook? _____

Check!

5 Answer these questions. You can find all the answers in Student's Book Unit 10.

1 What name are these people known by?

a _____ b _____

2 Complete this famous quotation of Neil Armstrong.

'That's one small _____ for man, one giant leap for _____.'

3 Which of these places have *the* in front of them?
a _____ Atlantic Ocean
b _____ Korea
c _____ Florida
d _____ USA
e _____ Moon

4 Read the sentence below. Match the underlined clauses with the correct type of relative clause (a or b).
a a defining relative clause
b a non-defining relative clause

Echolocation is a skill <u>which is also used</u> in the animal world, <u>where it is often key to survival</u>.

11a Conserving knowledge

Listening saving languages

1 💿 **89** Listen to a description of the work of Dr K. David Harrison and the 'Enduring Voices' team at *National Geographic*. Which sentence (a–c) best summarizes their work?

a   to help different people in the world to communicate with each other
b   to increase the number of languages spoken in the world
c   to save dying languages from extinction

2 💿 **89** Read the questions. Then listen again and choose the best option (a–c).

1   How many languages will there be in the world in 2050?
a   about 7,000
b   about 3,500
c   about 700

2   Bolivia is used as an example of a country with many languages because:
a   they are so different.
b   it has a large population.
c   it has as many languages as Europe.

3   Yuchi is a language spoken in Oklahoma which:
a   has only 70 speakers.
b   is a dead language.
c   people are trying to revive.

4   According to Dr Harrison, when we lose a language, we lose a culture's:
a   knowledge of the world.
b   important monuments.
c   stories.

5   Speakers of Yupik have helped us to understand better:
a   the geography of the Arctic.
b   their language and culture.
c   the effects of climate change.

6   The speaker thinks that globalization highlights the importance of:
a   diversity.
b   finding common interests.
c   saving dying languages.

3 💿 **89** Complete the summary of Dr Harrison's work using these words. Then listen again and check.

aim	centuries	diversity	express
extinct	huge	record	understand

Dr Harrison is part of a National Geographic project called Enduring Voices, whose [1] _____ is to document languages which are little known and are in danger of becoming [2] _____ . The race is on to trace and [3] _____ these languages. Dr Harrison seeks out places – language 'hotspots' – where there is a great [4] _____ of languages. This work is important because when we lose a language, we lose [5] _____ of thinking. All cultures [6] _____ their genius through their languages and stories. These languages store knowledge which can be of [7] _____ benefit to people today. For example, the Yupik language of the Eskimo people has helped scientists to [8] _____ how climate change is affecting the polar ice.

Grammar *could, was able to, managed to* and *succeeded in*

4 Look at these ideas from the description about the Enduring Voices project. Choose the correct option to complete the sentences.

1 Studies in the Oklahoma region of the USA *could discover / succeeded in discovering* 26 languages.

2 By highlighting this fact, researchers *could help / were able to help* the community to keep this dying language alive.

3 Some ancient cultures *could build / managed to build* large monuments by which we can remember their achievements.

4 A book written a few years ago by Yupik elders and scientists *was able to help / managed to help* other scientists to understand how climate change is affecting the polar ice.

5 One of the original arguments for globalization was that it *could bring / managed to bring* us all closer together.

6 He *could save / couldn't save* Ubykh – a language spoken near the Black Sea – from extinction.

5 Complete the sentences about learning a language using *could, was/were able to, managed to* or *succeeded in* and the verb in brackets. Sometimes more than one answer is possible.

1 The video I got was in Turkish, but I .... (find) English subtitles on the main menu.

2 My sister is an amazing linguist: she .... (speak) four languages fluently by the time she was twelve.

3 Esperanto was invented to be a world language, but supporters of it .... (not / convince) enough people to use it.

4 When I first moved to England, I .... (not / understand) native speakers because they spoke so quickly.

5 I had a friend who was brought up speaking three different languages, but I don't think he .... (express) himself clearly in any of them!

6 I learned Italian for eight years at school and .... (get) an 'A' grade in my exams. But when I tried to use it on holiday last year, I .... (only / remember) the grammar, not the vocabulary.

Vocabulary learning

6 Complete the words to make pairs of verbs with a similar meaning. The number of missing letters is in brackets.

1 understand and remember = t............... in (3)

2 pick up = a............... (6)

3 not know = be u............... of (6)

4 connect with = e............... with (5)

5 understand = g............... (2)

6 motivate = i............... (6)

7 Complete the sentences using a verb or expression from Exercise 6.

1 I didn't really learn Arabic while I was in Jordan, because most people spoke English, but I .... a few expressions.

2 She's a great teacher. She really knows how to .... her students.

3 I used to be completely .... how cars work, so I went on a basic mechanics course.

4 I .... the basics of car mechanics, but I couldn't repair an electronic fault.

5 I've explained the importance of punctuality, but Dan just doesn't seem to .... it.

6 Sorry, that's too much information to .... all at once. Can you go through it more slowly?

8 Dictation languages

a 🔊 90 Listen to someone talking about languages, place names and words. Write the words that they spell.

1 a .... b ....

2 a .... b ....

3 a .... b ....

4 ....

5 ....

b 🔊 90 Listen again and match the words from Exercise 8a with the correct meaning:

a a very long word in English ....

b the name of a college in the USA ....

c a word for an animal in a Siberian language ....

d an extinct language from the USA ....

e a new language found in India ....

11b Memory loss

Reading memory loss

1 Read the description of three types of memory loss quickly. Match the descriptions (1–3) with the summaries (a–c).

a   When you can't recognize someone you know

b   When your mind chooses to forget something it doesn't want to remember

c   When you have a false memory of something

2 Read the descriptions again. Are the sentences true (T) or false (F)? Or is there not enough information (N) to say if the statements are true or false?

1   Lacunar amnesia is when people have had a bad shock and don't remember what happened.

2   With lacunar amnesia, the memory completely disappears from the mind.

3   Sarah only remembers the moment when the truck hit the house.

4   Prosopamnesia is a condition some people inherit from their parents.

5   Philippa was concerned that the man who approached her was William Child.

6   William Child was just a colleague of Philippa's.

7   In source amnesia, people intentionally change the source of the memory.

8   In Jon's profession it is common to meet people with this condition.

9   The woman wanted her neighbour to be punished for the crime.

1 Lacunar amnesia

This literally means a gap in the memory. People who suffer from lacunar amnesia fail to remember a very specific event. It usually occurs when a person has suffered a traumatic event and their mind chooses to block it out. The memory is still there in fact, but our psychological defences stop us remembering the event to protect us from suffering further psychological trauma.

Sarah's story: 'When I was a child, something extraordinary happened at our house. My sister and I were just about to go to bed and I was downstairs saying goodnight to our parents. My sister was going to say goodnight to them too, but had gone to the kitchen to get a glass of water. At that moment, a truck ran into the ground floor of our house. I only know that because my sister, who was unhurt, told me afterwards. All I remember was saying goodnight, then waking up in hospital.'

2 Prosopamnesia

Prosopamnesia is an inability to remember faces. It is something that many people have in a mild form, but in severe cases, people can forget the faces of even close friends or associates. People can be born with this syndrome or it can be acquired during their lives.

Philippa's story: 'I'm terrible at remembering faces. I recall being at a conference at Berkeley University in California and another academic came up and started chatting to me. I would have asked his name, but knowing my inability to remember faces I didn't in case he was someone I was supposed to know. Anyway, it turned out that we had a friend and colleague in common. "Oh yes, I know William Child," I said. "We collaborated on a research project last year. He came to dinner at my house many times. How do *you* know him?" "I *am* William Child," the man replied.'

3 Source amnesia

Source amnesia occurs when a person is unable to recall where, when or how they learned something. In other words, they remember a fact, but they can't remember the context: where, when and how they learned it. A classic example of this is when people 'remember' something that happened to them when actually it happened to another person they know.

Jon's story: 'I work as a lawyer, and in my line of work I often come across people who have persuaded themselves of a version of events that may not be true. I had a witness who was going to give evidence in court that her neighbour had thrown a brick at her car. She clearly believed that this had happened, and was determined that her neighbour wasn't going to get away with it. But it turned out that it was not her own memory of events that she was describing, but what another neighbour had told her.'

3 Find phrasal verbs in the text on page 86 with the following meanings:

1 ignore something (para 1) ....

....

2 collided with (para 2) ....

3 approached (para 4) ....

4 became known (para 4) ....

....

5 find something (without expecting to) (para 6)

....

6 escape without punishment (para 6)

....

Grammar future in the past

4 There are six examples of the 'future in the past' forms in the text on page 86. Underline the examples. Which other future in the past forms could be used in these sentences? Sometimes the answer is 'none'.

1 *My sister and I were just about to go to bed … or were just going to go to bed …*

2 ....

3 ....

4 ....

5 ....

6 ....

5 Complete the sentences using a future in the past form. Sometimes more than one form is possible.

1 'I'm so sorry. I .... (write) you a letter, but I lost your address.'

2 'I .... (just / book) tickets to visit Munich, but then I remembered that it was Oktoberfest and all the hotels .... (be) full.'

3 'I promised her I .... (speak) to my boss about finding her a job, but I forgot.'

4 'The meeting .... (last) only an hour, but just as we .... (finish), Julian remembered that we hadn't discussed the move to our new offices.'

5 'I .... (take) my driving test sooner, but I didn't feel ready.'

6 'That's funny. I .... (just / ask) you exactly the same question.'

6 Pronunciation contrastive sentence stress

a 🔊 **91** Underline the words in the first half of the sentences that are most strongly stressed. Then listen and check.

1 I was going to email him, but I decided it would better to speak face to face.

2 He was supposed to get here early, but he's already ten minutes late.

3 I would have come by train, but there's a strike on at the moment.

4 She said she would be pleased if I talked to him, but she seemed really angry.

5 I was about to buy a flat, but Katie said I could rent hers for six months while she was away.

6 Liz was going to be in charge of the project, but now she's just acting as an advisor.

b 🔊 **91** Underline the words in the second half of the sentences in Exercise 6a that are most strongly stressed. Practise saying each sentence. Then listen again and check.

7 Grammar extra future phrases

> ▶ **FUTURE PHRASES**
>
> Notice that we use other phrases with the infinitive to talk about the future.
> She's **bound to** want to leave early.
> He's **likely to** change his mind.
> You're **unlikely to** find the information here.

Look at the grammar box. Then read the sentences (1–5) which talk about the future. Match the phrases in bold with the correct definition (a–e).

1 I'm sorry, but I always thought it was a terrible idea. It was **bound to** fail. ....

2 The plane was **due to** take off at 7 a.m., but poor weather meant it was delayed. ....

3 We thought that it was **unlikely** to be cold, so we didn't take any warm clothes with us.

....

4 It was **about to** rain so we decided to eat inside.

....

5 The political situation was **likely** to get worse, so we left the country for our own safety.

....

a not probable

b probable

c certain

d scheduled/expected

e on the point of

11c Intelligent animals

Listening

1 Match the name of the animal with the correct picture.

Bonobo monkey   border collie   crow
dolphin   scrub-jay

1 ....

2 ....

3 ....

4 ....

5 ....

2 🔊 **92** Listen to a description of five intelligent animals. Write the number of the animal (1–5) next to the intelligent behaviour that this type of animal is known for (a–e).

a They are good at copying what they see. ☐

b They are good at communicating. ☐

c They like to follow instructions. ☐

d They make plans for the future. ☐

e They make implements to get different jobs done. ☐

3 🔊 **92** Listen again and write the number of the animal (1–5) next to the intelligent action each animal did.

a found a clever way to reach some food ☐

b did acrobatics in time with one another ☐

c made food disappear ☐

d learned to match a two-dimensional image to a real object ☐

e cooked himself a treat ☐

4 Match these words from the descriptions with the adjectives (1–5).

inventive   mischievous   smart   expressive   playful

1 intelligent ....
2 creative ....
3 fun-loving ....
4 communicative ....
5 naughty ....

Word focus *learn*

5 Complete the sentences using expressions with *learn*.

1 You have to learn to .... before you can run.

2 It's never too .... to learn.

3 In life, you have to learn from your ....

4 I learned a few .... of the trade.

5 Never again. I've learned my ....

6 Just learn to .... with it!

7 I learned the hard ....

8 I've learned the whole poem by ....

11d Keep learning

Real life getting clarification

1 Complete these phrases with the correct verb.

1 What do you _____ by 'difficult'?
2 Can you _____ up a little? I can't hear you.
3 Can you _____ what the exam at the end of the course involves?
4 I'm sorry. I _____ not really with you.
5 Are you _____ that learning the historical dates isn't important?
6 Could you _____ me an example of an important historian of the last century?
7 There's a lot of information to _____ in.
8 I didn't _____ that last word. Can you repeat it?

2 🔊 **93** Listen to a conversation between a student and a college lecturer. Answer the questions.

1 What is the course?
_____

2 What is the student worried about?
_____

3 What does the lecturer recommend?
_____

3 🔊 **93** Listen again and complete the student's questions.

1 Can you explain _____
_____ ?
2 And are you saying that _____
_____ ?
3 Sorry, I'm not really with you. You mean _____
_____ ?
4 Could you give me an example of _____
_____ ?
5 Did you say _____
_____ ?

4 Grammar extra verbs with indirect objects

> ▶ **VERBS WITH INDIRECT OBJECTS**
>
> Some verbs, e.g. *tell* and *show* can be followed by an indirect personal object. Other verbs, e.g. *say* and *explain*, don't always need an indirect personal object. If you use an indirect personal object with these verbs, you must put *to* before the object.
>
> *He told **me** about the history course.*
> *I showed **him** a copy of the lecture notes.*
> *They explained (**to me**) that I could find the reading list online.*

Look at the grammar box. Complete the sentences by writing the pronoun *me* where necessary.

1 Can you tell _____ how many hours of study we're expected to do each week?
2 Do you recommend _____ that I should read Stephen Hawking's book?
3 She said _____ that I could get most of the books from the library.
4 She also explained _____ that the library was open until 10 p.m.
5 Can you show _____ how that works?
6 He taught _____ that I didn't always need to write such long essays.

5 Pronunciation linking in question forms

🔊 **94** Practise saying these sentences. Then listen and compare your pronunciation.

1 Did you say 'Africa'?
2 Could you explain that?
3 What do you mean by 'difficult'?
4 Can you give me an example?
5 What are you saying?

6 Listen and respond getting clarification

🔊 **95** Listen to a conversation between a teacher and a student (you). Respond with your own words. Then compare your response with the model answer that follows.

1
> So you wanted to ask me a question about the exam at the end of this course?

> Yes. Can you explain what the exam involves?

11e The wrong course

Writing an email about a misunderstanding

1 Match the two parts of the sentences about a misunderstanding over an application for a course. What seems to be the problem according to the writer?

1 The website said the deadline for entries was 20 August.

2 Despite the fact that my application arrived in time,

3 I am not someone who does things at the last minute.

4 While I appreciate that you have a lot of applicants for this course,

5 Whereas most colleges seem to select applicants on the merits of their application,

a you choose people on a 'first come, first served' basis.

b I cannot understand why you have chosen to ignore those people who applied after July.

c In fact, I sent in my application at the end of July.

d On the contrary, I am always careful to observe deadlines.

e I was told that I had missed the deadline.

2 Writing skill linking contrasting ideas

Rewrite these sentences from the reply to the applicant's letter using the words given.

1 We sympathize with your situation, but it is too late to do anything about it now. (while)

2 Despite the fact that you sent your form in before the deadline, we had already received too many applications. (although)

3 You say in your letter that we have no right to do this, but the college has the right to close the application process early. (in actual fact)

4 We are very careful to follow the rules. We don't 'make up the rules as we go along' as you suggest. (on the contrary)

5 Most colleges would keep your application fee, but we are refunding it to you. (whereas)

3 Look at the notes and write a letter to a college. Include the following points.

a Reason for writing: you can't attend the accountancy course this term.

b Misunderstanding: you thought it was an evening class, but it's during the day.

c Effort on your part: your company would like to give you time off, but they can't.

d Apology: probably your mistake, but these things happen.

e Action required: want the college to refund the money paid for the course fee.

Dear Sir / Madam

a

b

c

d

e

I look forward to

Yours

Wordbuilding homonyms

1 Match the homonyns with their meanings.

| company | point | room | spare | tip | value |

1 a the end (usually sharp) of an object
   b purpose _____ *point*

2 a a business organization
   b being with another person _____

3 a a small 'thank-you' payment
   b a piece of advice _____

4 a give something you have enough of (v)
   b extra or additional (adj) _____

5 a available space
   b a part of a building with walls and a ceiling
   _____

6 a importance of something
   b worth (in money) of a thing _____

2 Look at the underlined words in these sentences. Choose the correct meaning (a or b) from Exercise 1.

1 I don't see the <u>point</u> of this homework. __*b*__

2 There wasn't any <u>room</u> in the hall, so we had to stand. _____

3 I like her <u>company</u> a lot but we don't see each other much outside work. _____

4 Can I give you a <u>tip</u>? Always fill up your car with petrol before a long journey. _____

5 You can't under-estimate the <u>value</u> of hard work. _____

6 Can you <u>spare</u> some time to help next week? _____

Learning skills techniques for memorizing

3 People remember things in different ways. Sometimes you remember better by hearing, sometimes by seeing, and sometimes by doing or by action. It is important to know how you remember things. What do you remember of the following items in Unit 11?

1 The way children learn at the Lumiar school
   _____

2 How *could* is different from *managed to*
   _____

3 The intelligence of Alex, the grey parrot
   _____

4 Useful phrases for checking understanding
   _____

5 Expressions with the word *learn*
   _____

4 How did you remember the information in Exercise 3? By hearing, by seeing or by doing an action?

5 Look at these tips for memorizing. Tick (✓) the one(s) you feel suit you best.

a Write down five words that you need to learn. Give each a translation or put them into a sentence. Then listen to them again last thing at night.
b Draw a picture of the words that you need to learn. Look at the pictures the following day and see if you can remember the words.
c Work with another student and simulate a situation that illustrates the meaning of the word. Or think of an action that would help you remember the word.

6 Try to memorize these words and expressions from Unit 11 using the tips in Exercise 4.

| acquire Can you speak up? cramming |
| learn your lesson   my mind went blank |

Check!

7 Complete the sentences. Then use the FIRST letter of each word in sentences 1–6 to make the name of a Character from Unit 11. Use the SECOND letter of each word in sentences 7–10 to make the name of Character 2.

1 Another way to say 'we were able to do' something is 'we _____ in doing' it. (9)

2 At the Indianapolis Children's Museum kids could really _____ with the exhibits. (6)

3 When we have achieved a difficult task we say we have _____ to do it. (7).

4 'It's never too _____ to learn'. (4)

5 'We are more interested in people with practical _____ than good qualifications.' (10)

6 Another way of saying 'but in fact' is 'but in _____'. (7)

Character 1: _____

7 'Sorry, I didn't _____ your name.' (5)
8 'Who's a _____ bird, then?' (6)
9 If you learn something 'by _____', you can repeat it word for word. (5)
10 'Can you _____ what you mean?' (7)

Character 2: _____

Unit 12 Money

12a Save or spend?

Listening character and economics

1 🎧 **96** Listen to an economist giving his opinion about how character affects our attitude to money. Answer the questions.

1 Concerning attitudes to money, what two types of people does the economist describe?

....

2 Can we apply these characteristics to particular countries? Why? / Why not?

....

....

2 🎧 **96** Listen to the economist again and choose the best option (a–c) to complete the sentences.

1 People who are careful with money spend it:
   a when they see something they really want.
   b when it's for something of lasting benefit.
   c on what's necessary.

2 People who are extravagant with money ('spenders') say that they want to:
   a enjoy life while they can.
   b save but can't.
   c increase their possessions.

3 Some commentators said that certain countries who had borrowed money:
   a hadn't worked hard enough.
   b hadn't paid enough tax.
   c hadn't been careful with the money.

4 A lender faces the possibility of losing money and:
   a creating problems for the borrower.
   b going out of business.
   c waiting a long time for payment.

5 In most developed economies people want to:
   a be able to borrow money.
   b live more comfortably.
   c reduce their debts.

6 We need … to behave more responsibly.
   a spenders
   b savers
   c spenders and savers

3 Match the words in box A with a synonym in box B.

> **A** fund   prudent   transaction   wages   wasteful

> **B** careful   deal   extravagant   finance   salaries

Vocabulary the economy

4 Find and circle the words in the word search to complete these expressions.

1 the .... of living
2 the .... and the have ....
3 the .... gap
4 the .... of living
5 people's buying ....
6 .... of life

S	H	A	V	E	S	B
Q	U	A	L	I	T	Y
U	N	I	T	C	A	P
N	G	I	H	O	N	A
O	R	N	E	S	D	S
T	Y	C	Y	T	A	T
S	P	O	W	E	R	E
N	O	M	I	N	D	N
Y	D	E	L	I	V	E

Grammar focus adverbs *only, just, even*

5 Cross out the focus adverb that is in the incorrect position in these sentences.

1. Let's just consider just people's attitude to money at its simplest level.
2. Of course, savers spend only money, but only when they can afford it.
3. People in these countries even would have to work longer hours, pay more taxes and even accept lower wages.
4. You only don't only risk losing the money, but you also risk putting the borrower in a difficult situation.
5. We need both types of person, but only if they lend and borrow only responsibly.

6 Write the focus adverbs in the correct place in the sentences. There is sometimes more than one possible answer.

1. Some people believe that if you go through life saving money, you will never have any fun. ONLY

2. Some people carry on spending money when they can't afford to. EVEN

3. You can protect yourself against bad times by putting aside a small amount of money each week. JUST

4. If a few people save money, the banks won't have any money to lend to others. ONLY

5. It's not me who has debts; other people have them too. JUST

6. Some people say that your attitude to money is to do with your upbringing. JUST

7. Most people are careful with money when times are hard. ONLY

8. Some borrowers admit that sometimes they borrow money irresponsibly. EVEN

Vocabulary money

7 Complete these sentences with the correct noun. Use the verbs in brackets to help you.

1. To buy the car, I had to make _____ of £70 a month for five years. (pay)
2. We need to cut back on our _____ because the cost of living has become so high. (spend)
3. They say that gold is a good _____ at the moment. (invest)
4. We took out a _____ from the bank to finance the purchase of our apartment. (lend)
5. When I wanted to book my holiday, I used my _____ to pay for it. (save)
6. We wanted to increase our _____ so that we could build an extension on our house. (borrow)
7. The public _____ of the USA are counted in trillions of dollars rather than billions. (owe)
8. Public sector workers are protesting because their _____ haven't increased for the last two years. (earn)

8 Dictation money and lifestyle

🔊 **97** Listen to someone talking about money and lifestyle, and write down the words you hear.

I think that _____

It's a lifestyle _____

This desire _____

12b Cheap labour

Reading a history of industry

1 Read the article. What is the main message?
  a Cheap labour is always good for a country's economy.
  b Cheap labour is a benefit to the economy only if jobs stay in the country.
  c Businesses use cheap labour as a way of ensuring long-term success.

2 Read the article again. Are the sentences true (T) or false (F)? Or is the information not given (NG) to say if the sentences are true or false?

  1 A good exchange rate is the most important ingredient for a successful economy.
  2 The railway was invented in Britain.
  3 Britain was still the world's leading industrial power by the end of the 19th century.
  4 The American railways were built by people who had migrated to America from Europe.
  5 Companies have recently started looking for countries where they can pay people less to make their goods.
  6 It is cheaper to make things abroad because the cost of transporting goods is not too high.
  7 Making things at low cost abroad is good for both the company and the consumer.
  8 Even if some jobs go abroad from a country, better jobs will replace them in that country.

Cheap labour

There are three main ingredients for a successful economy. The first is a good exchange rate with the countries that you want to trade with. No one is going to buy your goods if they are too expensive. The second is technology. In the early 19th century, Britain became the dominant industrial power in the world because the Industrial Revolution started there and Britain was able to benefit from homegrown inventions like the railway and the mass production of goods. By the end of the same century, the USA was the dominant power, because they took the technological revolution forward with the telephone, the radio and then the aeroplane. In the early 20th century, Germany too became a major economy, developing its own new chemical and automobile industries.

Technological invention was very important for transforming the economies of Britain, the USA and Germany in this period, but their success would not have been possible without the third key ingredient – cheap labour. The history of successful economies has always been a story of cheap labour. If you can get people to work for not much money, your business will be more profitable. In 1830, the United States had only seventy kilometres of railway, but by 1890 it had over 250,000 kilometres. This was made possible by employing thousands of immigrants on low wages.

In more recent times, you can follow the movement of an industry – textiles and tuna canning are two striking examples – to the places where the work can be done more cheaply. Improved communications systems have meant that goods can be manufactured where labour costs are lowest and then transported at relatively low cost to the places (usually richer countries) where they are consumed. UK insurance companies have IT centres in Bangalore in India, French energy companies have call centres in Morocco, and US engineering companies have their machines produced in China and the Philippines.

However, there is a lot of debate now about whether this outsourcing of jobs to other countries is a good thing or not. In the short term, it is profitable for the companies that have their products made more cheaply, and it benefits their customers too. But does the decision to do this harm their own country's economy in the long term and cause unemployment among their own citizens? That is a question that remains to be answered.

3 Find words or expressions in the article on page 94 with the following meanings.

1 leading or powerful (para 1)

2 manufacturing in large quantities (para 1)

3 able to make money (para 2)

4 salaries (para 2)

5 bought and used (para 3)

6 places where large numbers of workers respond to phone calls (para 3)

7 paying someone else (i.e. another company) to do the work (para 4)

8 damage (v) (para 4)

Grammar causative *have* and *get*

4 Complete the sentences using the correct form of the words in brackets.

1 It's evident that if you can _____ (have / people / work) for very little money, your business is going to be more profitable.

2 Companies are always searching for ways they can _____ (get / their work / do) more cheaply.

3 A lot of western clothing firms _____ (have / their clothes / make) in India and Bangladesh.

4 A lot of tuna fishing companies _____ (get / their tuna / process) in the Philippines, Vietnam or Thailand.

5 You can _____ (get / most questions / answer) by a call centre operator. If they can't answer it, _____ (get / them / put) you through to a manager.

6 The economic argument for outsourcing is that you can _____ (get / anyone / do) the basic non-skilled jobs and then you can _____ (have / your own employees / do) the more skilled work.

5 Pronunciation the sounds /ʃ/, /tʃ/, /ʒ/ and /dʒ/

a 🔊 **98** Listen to these words from the article. Notice the pronunciation of the underlined sounds. Then complete the table.

cheap   deci<u>s</u>ion   ma<u>ch</u>ine   major
revolu<u>t</u>ion   ri<u>ch</u>er   u<u>s</u>ually   wages

/ʃ/	/tʃ/	/ʒ/	/dʒ/
wa<u>sh</u>	wat<u>ch</u>	plea<u>s</u>ure	chan<u>ge</u>

b 🔊 **99** Listen and check your answers to Exercise 5a.

Vocabulary getting things done

6 Complete the sentences about repairs to a house. Use the correct form of the verb. The first letter of each verb is given for you.

1 We need to get someone to f_____ this carpet. The shape of the room is so irregular.

2 I've asked John to p_____ up some new shelves in the living room. He's a professional carpenter.

3 I think we can d_____ the room ourselves. We don't need to have it done by a professional painter.

4 The kitchen units came in pieces and I had to a_____ them by myself. It took me about seven hours.

5 Can you call a roofer? The roof's still leaking and we need to get it f_____ .

6 You know that guy who t_____ our bathroom walls – he did a terrible job. There are cracks everywhere.

7 I'm going to get someone in to d_____ the gardening. It's just too much work for me.

8 We've just moved into a new flat and it's really dirty. I'm going to ring the agent and ask them to get it c_____ .

7 Look at these DIY jobs (1–6). Match the jobs with the professional (a–f) who does it.

1 fixing a leaky tap
2 rewiring a house
3 cutting the grass
4 demolishing a wall
5 fitting a new front door
6 painting the outside of a house

a a gardener
b a plumber
c a carpenter or joiner
d a general builder
e a decorator
f an electrician

12c The world of barter

Listening an interview

1 🔊 **100** Listen to an interview with a member of the Barter Society. What is the advantage of barter, according to him? Choose the correct option (a–c).

a You can exchange things without paying tax.
b It opens up a whole new world of people to do business with.
c You get a much better deal than you would if you used cash.

> **Glossary**
> **GDP** (n) /ˌdʒiːdiːˈpiː/ gross domestic product
> **spear** (n) /spɪə/ a long, pointed weapon used in hunting
> **tree surgeon** (n) /ˈtriː ˌsɜːdʒ(ə)n/ a specialist in cutting off damaged parts of trees

2 🔊 **100** Listen again and choose the best option (a–c) to complete the sentences.

1 The example of barter given by the interviewer is an exchange of a chicken for:
   a an item of clothing.
   b some food.
   c a weapon.

2 Barter is a system of trade that:
   a all primitive societies use.
   b is still used widely today.
   c has always had a small group of followers.

3 'Exchange barter' is a system:
   a that involves two people exchanging goods with one another.
   b that involves being a member of a club of other barterers.
   c where you exchange goods up to a certain value.

4 Barter exchanges:
   a aren't taxed.
   b are taxed if they are above a certain value.
   c are taxed in some countries.

5 The advantage of direct barter groups is that they:
   a mean you can reach a big group of potential customers.
   b allow you to pay less tax.
   c avoid currency exchange.

Vocabulary business words

3 Choose the correct options to complete the description of a hoverboard.

> A hoverboard is a two-wheeled motorized board that you stand and balance on. I don't think they will become very popular – I think they're just a(n) ¹ *upmarket / passing* fashion.
> The manufacturers have tried to create a ² *trend / buzz* around them, hoping that they will be the next big ³ *trend / recession*, but I don't think it will work. Part of the problem is the name: it seems quite ⁴ *catchy / upmarket*, but actually, hoverboards don't hover: they run on wheels. Another problem is the high price. A few ⁵ *loyal / passing* customers will continue to buy them, but at $300–400 each, it's a(n) ⁶ *catchy / upmarket* product that most people can't afford.

4 Grammar extra *hard* and *hardly*

> ▶ **HARD and HARDLY**
>
> The adjective *hard* has two different adverb forms: *hard* and *hardly*.
> I'm trying **hard** to see the advantage of it. (= I'm making a big effort.)
> There **hardly** seems to be any advantage in it. (= There is almost NO advantage in it.)
>
> Notice the position of *hard* and *hardly*: *hard* goes after the main verb and *hardly* goes before the main verb.

Look at the grammar box and compare the two sentences. Then complete these sentences using *hard* and *hardly* and the verbs in the correct form.

1 run / hard
   a He _____ . He'll be very fit if he manages to keep it up.
   b He _____ . It's more of a walk.

2 work / hard
   a She _____ now. She goes to the office once a week, I think.
   b She _____ now. She has a new boss who's very demanding.

3 know / hard
   I _____ him. We've met twice, I think.

4 think / hard
   a I _____ about it. It wasn't an easy decision.
   b I _____ about work when I was away on holiday.

5 try / hard
   a The team _____ . It was as if they didn't care.
   b The team _____ , but they weren't good enough to win.

12d The bottom line

Real life negotiating

1 Match the expressions (1–8) with phrases with the same meaning (a–h).

1 to tell you the truth
2 the key thing
3 let's face it
4 if I were in your shoes
5 at the end of the day
6 I'm sure you'll appreciate (that)
7 would you be willing to
8 isn't there some way around that

a what's important
b in your position
c are you happy to
d after considering everything
e we need to be realistic
f you must understand (that)
g can you see a solution
h to be honest

2 🔊 **101** Listen to two people in a negotiation and answer the questions.

1 What event are they discussing?

2 What does the client try to negotiate?

3 🔊 **101** Complete the phrases from the negotiation. Then listen again and check.

1 We want some food but, to be _____ , nothing too fancy.
2 OK, so what did you have in _____ ? A few canapés, some sandwiches?
3 Well, I was _____ we could have something a bit more exciting than sandwiches.
4 Yes, that _____ be much more like it.
5 That's quite a lot, but let's _____ it, it is an important occasion.
6 If I were in your _____ , I'd like to put on an event that people would remember.

7 You have to _____ that we have to come and set it all up and take it away anyway.
8 I see. Well, the _____ thing for us is that it's a nice relaxing event.

4 Pronunciation long vowel sounds

🔊 **102** Listen to the sentences. Which of the underlined vowel sounds are long (L) and which are short (S)?

1 OK, so what did you have in m*i*nd? ____
2 Perhaps if we prep*a*red some sushi … ____
3 Yes, that w*ou*ld be much more like it. ____
4 If I were in your sh*oe*s, … ____
5 The £10 also includes the w*ai*ting staff. ____
6 You have to appr*e*ciate that … ____
7 Well, the k*e*y thing for us is that … ____
8 Just let me know ex*a*ct numbers … ____

5 Grammar extra *would*

> ▶ **WOULD**
>
> The function of *would* is to make what you say sound more polite or diplomatic, so it is often used in negotiations.
> *Yes, that **would** be much more like it.*
> ***Would** that reduce the price a bit then?*

Look at the grammar box. Rewrite these sentences using *would* to make the sentences more diplomatic.

1 I'm afraid that will be difficult for me.

2 Can you move a bit on the price?

3 Are you willing to negotiate?

4 I need to have some kind of guarantee.

5 When do you need to know?

6 I don't want to put you to any trouble.

6 Listen and respond negotiating

🔊 **103** You are hiring a caterer to provide food at a party. Listen to what the caterer says and respond with your own words. Then compare your response with the model answer that follows.

1

> *So what kind of food did you have in mind? Some sandwiches?*

> *I was hoping we could have some hot food too.*

12e Get to the point

1 Writing skill key phrases in report writing

Complete the short report using these phrases.

As requested	Consequently	Initially
Overall	specifically	To sum up

¹ ...., here are some comments on the Media Hotel as a potential venue for our annual conference.

² ...., the hotel has excellent services and is in a great location, ten minutes from the seafront and a large number of restaurants. It is extremely comfortable and has very good conference facilities, ³ .... a large conference hall that seats 300 people and ten other well-equipped seminar rooms. However, on the weekend that I visited, the hotel had several groups of guests on hen and stag dos. ⁴ .... , it was very noisy and seemed more like a party venue. ⁵ .... I thought that this would rule out holding a conference there, but the manager assured me that on conference weekends, no such guests were permitted in the hotel.

⁶ .... , I think the Media Hotel is a possibility, but I would probably recommend looking at other options too.

Writing a short report

2 Read the short report on a training course. Where does this information (a–e) go in the report? Two pieces of information are used twice.

  a details of the course (2 places)
  b an introduction to the subject
  c summary of the course (2 places)
  d a suggestion for improvement
  e useful facts for future reference

As requested, ¹ .... on the one-day introductory course to website design that I attended last week at the County Further Education College.

Overall, it ² ...., although there were one or two things that could be improved. The teacher was very knowledgeable and had lots of experience of designing websites. We spent the first two hours looking at different website designs, specifically ³ .... Initially, I thought this took rather too long, but actually ⁴ ....

Then we were shown the basic tools for constructing a website. There are a lot of very good apps available for this purpose and the teacher showed us two of his favourites. The apps have clear instructions with them. Consequently, it's very easy ⁵ .... For the last hour of the day we were able to experiment with using some of these tools.

To sum up, I ⁶ .... Even if it doesn't tell you everything, it makes the idea of designing a website less frightening. However, I would have liked more ⁷ ....

3 Complete the report in your own words. Use your answers in Exercise 2 to help you.

1 ....
2 ....
3 ....
4 ....
5 ....
6 ....
7 ....

Wordbuilding *the* + adjective

1 Can you think of the right adjective for these groups of people in society?

1 People with a lot of money .... *the rich*
2 People without a job ....
3 People with very little money ....
4 People with nowhere to live ....
5 People over 70 ....
6 People who are well known ....
7 People who like adventure ....
8 People who work hard ....
9 People who don't work hard ....
10 People who are unwell ....

2 Which of the answers in Exercise 1 describe people in a positive situation (P), a negative situation (N), or neither positive or negative (X)?

Learning skills using the internet

3 The following ideas are ways you could use the internet to help you learn. Tick (✓) the ideas you could use.

1 Listen to or watch the news in English, e.g. on the BBC website. Note down key words as you listen to each story. Check their meaning online or in a dictionary. Then listen again.

2 Search for articles relevant to your interests on newspaper websites. Read the title and the first paragraph. Either mentally or on paper, note down two questions you would like answered by the article. Then read the article and find the answers.

3 If you are not sure how to pronounce a word, check in an online dictionary. Then practise saying it.

4 If you listen to English or American songs, search for the lyrics online. Follow them as you listen to the song. Look up any words you don't know.

5 Search for interesting quotations, sayings and anecdotes on websites. Try to memorize them.

4 Use the internet to find the following:

1 What does the word 'spin' mean in the context of political news?
....

2 How do you pronounce 'rhythm'?
....

3 What are the opening lyrics to 'Big Yellow Taxi' by Joni Mitchell?
....

4 a good quotation on the subject of 'success'
....

Check!

5 Complete the sentences about money and the economy using information from Unit 12. Then use the first letters of each word to make something that many of us dream of having!

1 The expression 'Saving for a .... day' means saving money in good times in preparation for more difficult times.

2 People use the term 'the .... gap' to refer to the difference in earnings between the rich and the poor.

3 Branding and a .... name are very important for any business. In my town, there is a Chinese restaurant called 'Wok and Roll'.

4 When we say that another person did a job for us we use the construction 'to get or .... something done'.

5 'At the .... of the day' is a commonly used phrase in negotiations.

6 The opposite of spending money is .... it.

Word: ....

LISTENING TEST

SECTION 1   *Questions 1–10*

Questions 1–3

Choose the correct letter, A, B or C.

> **Example**
>
> How did Martin first hear about the careers day?
> **A** his tutor made an announcement
> **B** he saw a notice advertising it
> **C** a friend told him about it

1   The careers day will be held
    A in the college where Martin studies.
    B in a public building.
    C in the open air.

2   How long does Martin plan to spend at the careers day?
    A a couple of hours
    B half the day
    C the full day

3   The Careers Day Website is available
    A to anyone who pays an additional fee.
    B only to those enrolled at the college.
    C for a limited period of time only.

Questions 4–5

Choose *TWO* letters *A–E*.

Which two activities are available during the lunch break?

    A advice on CV writing
    B talks by previous graduates
    C personal interviews with careers advisers
    D group discussions with recruitment agencies
    E video on opportunities to do voluntary work overseas

4   ....

5   ....

Questions 6–10

Complete the notes below.

Write **NO MORE THAN TWO WORDS AND/OR A NUMBER** *for each answer.*

	CAREERS DAY Scheduled Talks		
Time	Faculty	Speaker	Topic
10.00	Law	Professor **6**	contracts of employment
11.00	**7**	Professor Smith	internships
11.00	Languages	Dr Sally Wentworth	**8** ....
13.00	Lunch break		
14.00	Engineering	Dr Shah	opportunities in the **9** ....
15.00	Sports Science	Professor Bellucci	Olympic Games
16.00	**10**	Dr Fulton	interview techniques

SECTION 2

Questions 11 and 12

Choose the correct letter, A, B or C.

11 If you visit Jodrell Bank, you can
     A walk close to the telescope.
     B go on a guided tour of the buildings.
     C meet the scientists who work on the site.

12 A family ticket in the winter costs
     A £19.50.
     B £20.
     C £25.

Questions 13 and 14

*Choose **TWO** letters A–E.*

Which two facilities are currently available at the visitor centre?

     A cinema
     B lecture theatre
     C interactive displays
     D refreshments
     E planetarium

13 ....

14 ....

Questions 15–20

Complete the table below.

*Write **NO MORE THAN TWO WORDS AND/OR A NUMBER** for each answer.*

History of Jodrell Bank	
Year	Event
1939	The site was purchased by the university's **15** .... department.
1945	Bernard Lovell moved some radar equipment to the site. Installation coincided with a **16** ...., which Lovell observed.
17	Giant Transit Telescope built at Jodrell Bank.
1957	The telescope was replaced by one originally called the **18** .... Telescope.
1972	Arboretum created featuring a scale model of the **19** ....
2011	New visitor centre opened. Jodrell Bank proposed as a possible **20** .... site.

SECTION 3

Questions 21–24

*Choose the correct letter, **A**, **B** or **C**.*

21 When asked if the elective is like a holiday, Damian
    A suggests that this depends on the individual.
    B admits that he spent too much time enjoying himself.
    C denies that his placement was unusual in this respect.

22 Why did Damian find it hard to organize his elective?
    A He had never travelled alone.
    B He was unfamiliar with other cultures.
    C He wasn't sure what he wanted to specialize in.

23 How does Damian feel about splitting his elective between two places?
    A He wishes he hadn't decided to do that.
    B He thinks he spent too long in one place.
    C He insists that he made the right decision.

24 When choosing a company to help him find an elective placement, Damian
    A relied on word-of-mouth recommendations.
    B did thorough research on the Internet.
    C tried not to be influenced by price.

Questions 25 and 26

Complete the sentences below.

*Write **NO MORE THAN TWO WORDS** for each answer.*

Damian decided to look for an elective placement specializing in **25** .... medicine.

Damian chose Belize because he was impressed by pictures of the **26** .... there.

Questions 27–30

Complete the notes below.

*Write **NO MORE THAN THREE WORDS** for each answer.*

> BELIZE
>
> Total population: **27** ....
>
> Area where Damian worked: **28** ....
>
> Nationality of most doctors: **29** ....
>
> What Damian would do if he returned to Belize: **30** ....

SECTION 4

Questions 31–35

Complete the notes below.

Write **NO MORE THAN THREE WORDS** *for each answer.*

Antiguan Racer Snake	
Length:	31 ....
Colouring of male:	32 ....
Colouring of female:	33 ....
Preferred habitat:	34 ....
Diet:	35 ....

Questions 36–38

Complete the sentences below.

Write **NO MORE THAN TWO WORDS** *for each answer.*

Until 1995, the snake was thought to be extinct.

In 1995 it was rediscovered living on **36** .... island.

A **37** .... was commissioned by the Antiguan Forestry Unit.

An estimated **38** .... racer snakes were found to be living on the island.

In 1996, a long-term conservation project was founded.

Questions 39 and 40

What still poses a threat to the snakes?

Choose **TWO** *letters A–E.*

    A disease
    B the extent of its habitat
    C severe weather events
    D predation by rats
    E expansion of tourism

39 ....

40 ....

READING TEST

SECTION 1

You should spend about 20 minutes on Questions 1–10, which are based on the text below.

How to get a grant for scientific research

In applying for a research grant, it's essential to start by identifying the appropriate granting body to contact for your proposal, as each body usually has its own particular priority areas. Once you've done this, check you can meet both the eligibility criteria and the deadline for the submission of applications. Your proposal should be written out in the format stipulated by your chosen organization. Almost all granting bodies now have electronic application forms posted on the Internet, although these can sometimes be both complex and cumbersome.

A grant request is generally broken down into the following components:

Objectives

Succinctly describe your research goal, and what you propose to do to achieve this. It's a good idea to propose only those objectives that you feel relatively confident of achieving within the grant period. A proposal with too many objectives to be included in a relatively short time is likely to be considered over-ambitious, and might well be rejected, even if it involves cutting-edge science or a revolutionary new idea.

Background and rationale

Introduce the problem that the research intends to address. The length of your description is dictated by the length limitations on the application form. You should cover what is already known about the problem in the scientific literature, and highlight the major gaps or limitations in the current knowledge base. The final paragraph should state precisely what you will have achieved if the project succeeds, and the likely impact of a successful research project. In addition, many application forms, even for basic research grants, now have a section in which you're required to describe how the research is likely to contribute to economic development.

Experimental design and methods

You must describe in detail exactly what you're going to do to achieve your stated objectives. You should provide sufficient details to enable the review panel to critically evaluate your project. In particular, you must show how the experimental design will answer the questions that you're setting out to address; poor experimental design is the downfall of many applications.

Critical appraisal and limitations of the proposed approach

Describe the possible limitations of your proposed approach. For example, one of your proposed methodologies may have certain disadvantages that could impact adversely on your findings. A reviewer will certainly point this out and might find it sufficient grounds for rejecting your proposal. To meet such concerns, you should therefore state clearly that you're aware of the limitations of your approach, and if possible propose an alternative strategy if your first approach fails to deliver. You should also describe briefly any particular strengths of your laboratory likely to contribute to the success of the project if it is funded.

Questions 1–10

Do the following statements agree with the information given in the text?

In boxes 1–10 on your answer sheet, write

TRUE	*if the statement agrees with the information*
FALSE	*if the statement contradicts the information*
NOT GIVEN	*if there is no information on this*

1   Find the granting body which is best suited to the type of research you want to do.

2   Find out the date by which proposals must be sent in.

3   It's a good idea to lay out your proposal in an imaginative way.

4   Your proposal should have a long-term aim that extends beyond the timescale of the grant.

5   Make sure you fill all available space on the application form.

6   Your application should refer to other work already carried out on your topic.

7   It's essential to say how your research is relevant to economic and social issues.

8   The review panel may contact you with questions about your experimental design.

9   It's better to be honest if you have any doubts about aspects of your proposal.

10   You should give a full description of any laboratory facilities available to you.

Questions 11–16

The text on page 107 has six sections, **A–F.**

*Choose the correct heading for sections **A–F** from the list of headings below.*

Write the correct number (i–ix) in boxes 11–16 on your answer sheet.

List of Headings

i	Research experience
ii	Laboratory investigations
iii	Preliminary data
iv	Background reading
v	Description of the study area
vi	Data analysis
vii	Subject recruitment
viii	Collaboration
ix	Data collection

11   Section **A** ....

12   Section **B** ....

13   Section **C** ....

14   Section **D** ....

15   Section **E** ....

16   Section **F** ....

Experimental design and methods

Within this section of your research proposal, there should be several sub-sections, some of which are required for all types of grants, others of which are dependent on the topic of the research.

A Granting bodies like to see a concise description of the results of any work you have already carried out towards the research. Focus on the results that suggest that the proposed work will probably succeed.

B If the proposed research involves field studies, your application should include latitude and longitude, elevation, vegetation, rivers, rainy and dry seasons, mean rainfall and temperatures, and distance from the capital city.

C Describe how you plan to find people to take part in experiments and what criteria you will use for including or excluding particular individuals. Most importantly, include how you will obtain informed consent from these people, and which national authority or authorities have given ethical approval for your research.

D It is important to provide sufficient detail in this section for the reviewer to agree that the proposed work is feasible. There is no need to go into a lot of detail if the laboratory procedures that you plan to use are standard and widely described in scientific literature. However, you must still provide some details of your proposed procedures. Make sure you include a brief description of the various analytical techniques that you will carry out.

E This should include how it will be entered into a computerised database and what software will be used. In the case of trials, you should include how various variables, either continuous or discrete, will be compared among different groups studied using a variety of statistical methods, and how you intend to control for confounding variables.

F It is important to identify the partners with whom you intend to work, either in your own country or overseas. The choice of research partner or partners is crucial for your research project. They should provide complementary, rather than identical, expertise and/or facilities, and it must be clear how their presence will strengthen your proposal.

SECTION 2

You should spend about 20 minutes on Questions 17–27, which are based on the text below.

The world's oldest mattress

A study published in *Science* by Lyn Wadley of the University of Witwatersrand and her colleagues throws new light on the behaviour of early man in South Africa. The focus of the research is a cave in a natural rock shelter called Sibudu, situated in a sandstone cliff, 40 kilometres north of Durban. Dr Wadley has found evidence for at least 15 separate occasions when it acted as a home, with periods in between when it was abandoned, as is often the case with such shelters. Each occupation left debris behind, though, and as this accumulated, the cave floor gradually rose. All told, these layers reveal occupation over a period of about 40,000 years.

Among the things Dr Wadley's team found in the floor of the cave was evidence of mat making throughout the period of habitation. The oldest stratum, dating from 77,000 years ago, predate other known instances of plant matting by approximately 50,000 years. They consisted of compacted stems and leaves of plants stacked in layers within a chunk of sediment three metres thick.

'The inhabitants would have collected the plant matter from along the river, located directly below the site, and laid the plants on the floor of the shelter,' said Wadley. The lower part of these layers, compressed to a thickness of about a centimetre, consists of sedges, rushes and grasses. The upper part, just under a millimetre thick, is made of leaves from *Cryptocarya woodii*, a tree whose foliage contains chemicals that kill biting insects. Dr Wadley thus thinks that what she has found are mattresses on which the inhabitants slept, although they may also have walked and worked on them.

The upshot is another piece of evidence of how, around this period, humans were creating a range of hitherto unknown artefacts. Adhesives, arrows, needles, ochre-decorated pictograms and necklaces made from shells are all contemporary with Dr Wadley's finds, and stone tools became more delicate and sophisticated during this period.

Indeed, given the age of the mats and other artefacts at the site, it's clear that *Homo sapiens* was the hominid who slept in the cave. The earliest hominids had very different sleeping accommodations. Even though they had evolved an efficient way to walk on the ground, hominids such as *Australopithecus* were still small, not much bigger than a chimpanzee. They probably settled in trees at night, for if they slept on the ground, they would have been vulnerable to nocturnal predators looking for a midnight meal. The fossils of early hominids indicate this was possible; they still retained features useful for climbing, such as curved fingers and long arms. Once in the trees, they probably built nests of branches, twigs and leaves, just as chimpanzees do today.

The first hominid to try the ground as a bed might have been *Homo erectus*, starting almost two million years ago. Richard Wrangham, a biological anthropologist at Harvard University, suggests that once hominids learned how to control fire they discovered they could sleep on the ground while the flames kept predators away. It was also useful for cooking and processing foods, allowing *Homo erectus* to expand its diet. Adaptations for arboreal life were eventually lost, and *Homo erectus* became bigger and taller, the first hominid with a more modern body plan. Although there's no evidence in the paleontological record that hints at what type of bedding *Homo erectus* used, modern humans were certainly not the only hominids to construct 'mattresses'. Neanderthals were also building grass beds, based on evidence from a cave site in Spain dating to between 53,000 and 39,000 years ago.

Questions 17–19

*Choose the correct letter, **A**, **B**, **C** or **D**.*

Write your answers in boxes 17–19 on your answer sheet.

17 Dr Wadley believes that the cave at Sibudu was lived in
    A continuously over many thousands of years.
    B on a surprising number of different occasions.
    C intermittently during a long period of pre-history.
    D at times when other dwellings had to be abandoned.

18 Why is the evidence of mat making at Sibudu particularly significant?
    A It reflects findings in similar caves elsewhere.
    B It's older than other examples of similar craft skills.
    C It proves that the caves were actually once inhabited.
    D It helps establish the period when the caves were in use.

19 What leads Dr Wadley to think that the mats were used for sleeping?
    A one of the materials from which they were made
    B the thickness of the strata that were created
    C the use of plant matter collected nearby
    D the fact they were constructed in layers

Questions 20–22

What other artefacts from the same period as Sibudu are mentioned in the text?

*Write the correct three letters **A–G** in boxes 20–22 on your answer sheet.*

    A illustrations
    B building materials
    C weapons
    D sewing equipment
    E fastenings for clothing
    F cooking equipment
    G cleaning materials

20 ....

21 ....

22 ....

Questions 23–27

Complete the sentences below.

*Choose **NO MORE THAN TWO WORDS** from the passage for each answer.*

Write your answers in boxes 23–27 on your answer sheet.

Australopithecus probably used **23** .... as places to sleep.

Early hominids had physical features that suggest they were good at **24** ....

Early hominids may have constructed nests similar to those made by **25** ....

Homo erectus used **26** .... for protection whilst sleeping.

Neanderthals may have used **27** .... to make a surface to sleep on.

You should spend about 20 minutes on Questions 28–40, which are based on the text below.

HUMAN MEMORY AND BRAIN FUNCTION

In recent years there has been growing support for the idea that the human brain is comparable to a muscle which will grow and develop given appropriate exercise. This form of 'brain training' is said to include a wide variety of mental exercises from crossword puzzles and numbers games to learning a language and writing stories. Indeed, a new industry is emerging as businesses produce programmes designed to assist people – particularly the elderly – who want to improve their brain function or slow its decline. However, the brain training industry has attracted some controversy. In 2014 a group of more than sixty cognitive psychologists and neuroscientists signed a document stating that the brain training industry took advantage of people's anxieties and was not supported by sufficient research.

Nonetheless, there is a growing body of science behind brain training. For example, the Nun Study showed that subjects who had worked as teachers reached old age with more advanced cognitive abilities than those who had worked in manual jobs. This may be related to how the brain actually operates. In a 2015 survey of the general public, the majority of respondents believed that memory was a natural element of brain function, but in reality the brain is programmed to forget information in case it becomes overloaded. Thus, it may be possible to alter this programming using mental stimulation exercises in order to improve memory. Certainly, evidence is mounting that human memory is extremely complex. The Memory Foundation is a project with some 10,000 members who practise brain training. It recognizes six key types of memory – including remembering words and faces – all of which are equally significant and will respond positively, it is claimed, to brain training.

Research by the Mayo Clinic is also encouraging. The Clinic conducted a study on elderly subjects who all carried the gene for Alzheimer's disease (APO-E4) but were otherwise in good physical health. Brain imaging demonstrated that subjects who remained mentally active showed fewer symptoms of the disease. Similarly, initial results from a study in New Zealand called Memory Lane recorded positive effects of brain training on different aspects of human memory. The Memory Lane study is now being transferred to the University of Auckland where the data will be analysed by a team of specialists.

What is becoming apparent is that there are a variety of different beliefs about the role of brain training. One of those working in this field is Professor Michael Merzenich of the University of California. He has designed a range of techniques and exercises which aim to increase the speed with which the brain can process information. Professor Merzenich believes that the benefits of his brain training techniques are evident in simple activities that everyone does on a routine basis, such as listening. 'What good is it to train your brain if it doesn't apply to your everyday life?' he asks. Driving is another such commonplace skill that studies show has been enhanced by Merzenich's techniques. Professor Merzenich is now involved in various trials to test the wider potential of brain training. One promising line of research suggests that those who have suffered a serious head injury appear to respond positively. He also hopes that in years to come these techniques might be used with offenders who have been sent to prison, in order to equip them with better skills when they are released.

Melanie Cheung, a University of Auckland neurobiologist, is investigating the decline in brain function associated with a serious neurological condition. She has concluded that conventional medication is ineffective for treating many of the symptoms she observes. Cheung is in the second year of a three-year research project, working with subjects aged from 18 to 65. Most of them are initially enthusiastic to try brain training but Cheung admits that it can be difficult for them to maintain sufficient motivation to keep working at the techniques because improvement may take a long time to become apparent.

Related research is being conducted by Gary Small, professor of psychiatry at the University of California. He argues that brain function will certainly be promoted by regularly exercising both body and mind, but there are also other factors involved, notably the role of proper nutrition, that have been overlooked so far. And while there is certainly plenty of optimism about the potential of brain training, researcher Madeleine Crompton has a word of caution. Crompton runs a range of programmes designed for those aged over 65 and says that one issue is that doctors seldom see the value in her techniques or recommend them to their patients. If this obstacle could be overcome, she believes, the benefits of brain training could be experienced much more widely in society.

Questions 28–33

Do the following statements agree with the claims of the writer of the text?

In boxes 28–33 on your answer sheet, write

YES	*if the statement agrees with the claims of the writer*
NO	*if the statement contradicts the claims of the writer*
NOT GIVEN	*if it is impossible to say what the writer thinks about this*

28 Some academics are critical of the brain training industry.

29 The results of the Nun Study surprised the participants in the study.

30 A 2015 survey found that most people misunderstand human brain function.

31 The Memory Foundation believes some types of memory are more important than others.

32 The Mayo Clinic study investigated subjects with a range of medical problems.

33 The Memory Lane study should have used a larger sample of subjects.

Questions 34–40

Complete the notes below.

Choose **ONE WORD ONLY** from the text for each answer.

Write the answers in boxes 34–40 on your answer sheet.

Different Beliefs about Brain Training

Professor Merzenich

- brain training improves everyday skills like listening and **34** ....
- people who have had a bad **35** .... seem to benefit from brain training
- it is possible that in future brain training may help people in **36** ....

Melanie Cheung

- **37** .... is not the solution when brain function is decreasing
- having high enough levels of **38** .... can be a problem for brain training

Other Researchers

- Professor Small: mental and physical exercise and good **39** .... affect brain function
- Madeleine Crompton: **40** .... need to recognize the benefits of brain training for the elderly

WRITING TEST

TASK 1

You should spend about 20 minutes on this task.

You have recently gone to live in a new city.

Write a letter to your English-speaking friend. In your letter
- *explain why you have gone to live in the new city*
- *describe the place where you are living*
- *invite your friend to come and see you*

Write at least 150 words.

You do not need to write any addresses.

Begin your letter like this:

Dear Anna,

TASK 2

You should spend about 40 minutes on this task.

Write about this topic.

The ownership of cars should be restricted to one per family in order to reduce traffic congestion and pollution.

To what extent do you agree or disagree?

Give reasons for your answer and include any relevant examples from your own knowledge or experience.

Write at least 250 words.

SPEAKING TEST

PART 1 – INTRODUCTION AND INTERVIEW

Let's talk about how you keep in touch with world events.
- How do you usually find out what is happening in the world?
- Are you more interested in national news or world news? Why (not)?
- What do you do if you want to find out more details about a news item (and why)?
- Do you think reading or listening to the news in English is a good idea?

PART 2 – INDIVIDUAL LONG TURN

Candidate Task Card

Describe a time when you took part in an experiment or a piece of research.

You should say:
  what the aim of the experiment or piece of research was
  why you became involved in it
  what your role in it was
and explain how you felt about taking part.

You will have to talk about the topic for one to two minutes.

You will have one minute to think about what you are going to say.

You can make some notes to help you if you wish.

Rounding off questions
- Do you know what the outcome of the experiment/research was?
- Would you take part in that sort of experiment/research again?

PART 3 – TWO-WAY DISCUSSION

Let's consider first of all the role of scientific research.
- How important is scientific research?
- Which type of scientific research do you think is most important (and why)?
- Do you think too much money is spent on exploring outer space? Why (not)?

Finally, let's talk about how scientific research is reported by the media.
- Do you think that the media reports scientific research accurately? Why (not)?

Audioscripts

Unit 1

1

P = Presenter, E = Expert

P: I'd like to ask you two questions: what is the real reason for the ageing population? And secondly, and more importantly, what effect is this having on relationships in society?

E: Well, there's not just one reason; there are a number of them. Firstly, the birth rate has declined over the last twenty years – people are having fewer children. The second reason is that sixty years ago, there was a baby boom; these 'baby boomers' are now reaching retirement age. So there are lots of retirees around and not so many young people. There's also no doubt that people's diets have improved: generally we are more knowledgeable about what foods are healthy and unhealthy. Also, in recent years, governments have obliged food producers to give consumers information about the fat and salt content of their food. Actually, I'd say in general that people have a healthier lifestyle than they did in the past: they eat better and they've also learned the right way to exercise and keep fit. Lastly, we can't underestimate the enormous progress that medical science has made in improving the health of old people. People can now get treatment for life-threatening diseases. We didn't have things like flu jabs or pacemakers fifty years ago. These advances have increased life expectancy to around eighty in the developed world. Fifty years ago, it was closer to seventy.

P: And what are the social consequences of this ageing population – that in the West there are many more old people than young people?

E: Well, the main result is that a smaller number of young people now have to support a growing number of old people. Also people are working longer: in the last ten years, the retirement age has risen from around 62 to 67. Not only that, but they've been spending more time looking after elderly parents. That, of course, puts a strain on family relationships because parents who spent twenty years bringing up their own children then find they are spending the next ten looking after their own ageing parents. That means less time together as a couple and less free time to enjoy with other friends and family. It's not easy …

3

1 I think my parents' generation has been quite lucky.
2 My parents worked hard all their lives, but they both retired when they were sixty and the government has given them good pensions. So now they can relax and enjoy themselves.
3 They've said that they don't want to be a burden on us, and that they don't expect us to look after them when they get old.
4 Considering that my husband and I will probably have to work until we are 68, I'm glad they said that.

4

P = Presenter, L = Lauren

P: I know that Vietnam is a country which is developing incredibly fast and Lauren, you've just been sent on a three-week trip there as part of your university course …

L: That's right, yes.

P: … which sounds fantastic. I wish my economics degree had included that kind of trip, but … Can you just tell us a bit about how people in Vietnam are adapting to those huge changes and what it all means for them?

L: Sure. As you say, Vietnam is a very dynamic society right now. It's being transformed at an amazingly fast rate – both economically and socially. We were really lucky to get to experience that first-hand and get to meet so many different people of all ages, from all kinds of work backgrounds – politicians and government officials, farmers, and so many just … regular people too. And I've got to say – if anyone's thinking of going there – the people are amazing: really warm and friendly. But to answer your question, I think what you have is an older generation who are very conscious of their history. Many of them have been through two wars and are very aware of how much they've struggled to get to this point now of, of relative prosperity. And then there's a younger generation and they don't necessarily see all that effort. They kind of take this new wealth and opportunity for granted. I think they see the world opening up and they really want a part of it. And that's not always easy, because there are still some restrictions on access to information – Facebook and other social networking sites are closed down from time to time, for example. On the other side, the older generation desperately want their children and grandchildren to understand Vietnam's history and be proud of it, and of course to respect Vietnamese traditions.

P: And did you get a sense that people are confused by this? That they don't know which way to turn, as it were?

L: You know, not really. The sense I got was that the gap between old and young is being bridged by the generation in the middle – I guess the 30- and 40-somethings. We spent a day in a fishing community near the Mekong Delta and we had a meal with a family there, and all the generations were getting on fine together. I had the impression that the parents kind of balanced the home. The grandparents are really included and involved in things – they get to take care of the grandchildren and to teach them what they know. You could see that really clearly. And at the same time, the grandparents are definitely listened to and treated with respect by the parents and the children. I was really impressed by that, especially when you compare it with …

7

B = Ben, S = Sam

B: Hi Sam. Fancy bumping into you here. I've been wondering how you were.

S: Oh, hi, Ben. What a nice surprise. I'm fine. I've been working in Scotland for the last three months.

B: Well, it obviously suits you. You're looking very well. Have you decided to move up there?

S: No, it's just a temporary job. I've been helping to renovate an old castle. And how's it all going with you? Is Emily well?

B: Yes, thanks. She's just finished her nursing course.

S: Really? That's fantastic. Do give her my best regards.

B: Well, great to see you. I should probably go and do my shopping.

S: OK. Could I have your phone number again? I've lost it.

B: Sure. It's 07945 699636.

S: Thanks. Well, speak soon, I hope. Good luck with the job.

8

1 How are things?
2 I'm doing fine, thanks.
3 You're looking very well.

4 It's been ages.
5 I should probably get back to work.
6 Sorry, I've got to rush.

9
F = Friend, MA = Model answer
1
F: Hi. What a nice surprise! How are you?
MA: I'm fine, thanks. Good to see you.
2
F: So, what have you been up to lately?
MA: I've been working quite hard, but everything's going well.
3
F: Well, it obviously suits you. You're looking well.
MA: Thanks. So are you.
4
F: And do you see much of the old crowd these days?
MA: I've seen Polly a few times.
5
F: Well, I don't mean to be rude, but I need to get to the bank.
MA: No problem. Great to see you.

Unit 2

10
On April 25, 2003, Aron Ralston drove to Moab, Utah, where he mountain-biked the famous Slickrock Trail. He then made his way to Horseshoe Canyon. When he arrived, night was falling, so he made camp. He was planning an ascent of Mount McKinley in Alaska, and this trip was part of his training. In the morning, he filled his backpack with water, candy bars and his climbing gear, and set out for Bluejohn Canyon.

He climbed into the canyon on April 26. He had gone about five miles when he came to a section where a series of large boulders were hanging, wedged between the walls of the canyon. He worked his way past these until he came to a boulder hanging over a drop of about three metres. Putting one hand around the boulder, which weighed about 800 pounds, Ralston stretched to reach a secure foothold below. As he did so, the boulder rotated, slid down and trapped his right hand between it and the canyon wall, crushing it completely.

His heart was beating fast and for the first few moments he threw his body repeatedly against the boulder to move it, but it refused to move. He forced himself to stop, breathe and then considered his situation logically.

He hadn't told anyone where he was. It would be days before anyone realized that he was missing. Ralston was standing on a small stone, facing the boulder that had crushed his hand. The pain was intense, but he was determined to stay in control. He only had two courses of action left to him: he could chip at the rock to free his hand; or he could cut off his hand.

His only tool was a cheap multi-tool. Over the next days, he worked to chip away at the rock with it, but the progress he made was minimal. He was wearing shorts, hiking boots and a fleece pullover. He had started with three litres of water. Now he was down to one.

Ralston had been waiting there for five days. But by the time the search teams started out, he had long since decided what he had to do. He packed his gear and arranged everything neatly in preparation for cutting off his hand. The arm was numb, so he didn't feel anything, but it was still not an easy thing to do. The operation took over an hour. Dripping blood, he made his way back out of the canyon and began the long hike out of the National Park. After six miles, he was met by some tourists.

11
1	crashed	3	stuck	5	sung
2	top	4	cat	6	drunk

13
1 The setting for Alain de Botton's thought-provoking book, *A Week at the Airport*, is Heathrow airport.
2 The characters are you and me and every other typical passenger that passes through the airport.
3 The book is based on conversations that the author had with travellers and airline staff.
4 The idea behind it is that if you are looking for somewhere that can portray modern civilization, you don't need to look any further than an airport.

14
Part 1
Oscar Wilde's collection of short stories *The Happy Prince and other Stories* is for children, but like all good children's literature, the stories have been written in a way that appeals to children and adults alike. The stories contain elements of a traditional fairy tale – giants, speaking animals, often a message too. But they are not just good stories. They also have a strange kind of beauty about them and often this beauty lies in their sadness. I remember being sad when I heard them as a child and when I read them again to my children a few years ago, I still had to keep back the tears. It's impossible not to be moved by them. As to their message, Oscar Wilde didn't want to give moral lessons. He just wanted to describe human behaviour and leave the reader to make up their own mind. Let me give you an example – the story of *The Happy Prince*.

Part 2
The Happy Prince is a metal statue that stands high in the square of an old town in northern Europe. It's a beautiful statue covered in gold and the Prince has jewels for eyes and jewels in his sword. From where he stands, he can see everything that is happening in the town, good and bad.

One day, a little swallow arrives, flying on its way south to a warmer climate in Egypt for the winter. He stops to rest on the shoulder of the Happy Prince and the prince asks him for his help. He begs the swallow to take the gold and jewels from his statue to various people around the town who are poor or in need: a little boy selling matches in the street, a poor artist in his cold attic room. The swallow stays for some days keeping the prince company and taking these precious things to people until he has taken all the gold and jewels from the statue. By now it has got too late and too cold for the swallow to continue its journey, and it gets sick and dies at the base of the statue. The town councillors come by and see the statue all grey and plain-looking with a dead bird lying at its feet. Since it no longer looks beautiful, they decide to pull it down and melt it so that the metal can be turned into something useful. At the metal foundry, the workers find one part won't melt – the Happy Prince's heart – and they throw it on the rubbish tip where the dead swallow is lying.

15

See track 14, Part 1

16

See track 14, Part 2

17

A = Friend 1, B = Friend 2
A: How was the trip?
B: Well, we had a great time once we got there, but the journey there was a complete nightmare.
A: Oh no. Poor you! What happened?
B: Well, about four hours before we were due to leave, Hannah realized that her passport was out of date.
A: Oh, that's awful. So did you leave her behind?
B: No, Paul took her straight to the passport office in London and someone had just cancelled their appointment, so they were able to get Hannah a new passport within an hour.
A: That was a stroke of luck. And where were you?
B: I went to the airport to wait for them and kept in touch with them by phone.
A: How stressful! Did they make it in time?
B: Well, they wouldn't have done but the plane was delayed by two hours, so in the end they got there with a bit of time to spare. But my nerves were completely destroyed by then.
A: I can sympathize. I hate being late when I'm travelling. Did the rest of the trip go OK?
B: Yeah, it was great, thanks. Costa Rica was fabulous. But I made sure we got to the airport four hours early for the flight back.
A: Did you? I don't blame you. I think I would have done the same thing.

20

F = Friend, MA = Model answer
1
F: You'll never guess what happened to me yesterday on the bus. I started talking to this woman who I thought was Sue, my next-door neighbour, about my problems at work. But it wasn't Sue, it was a complete stranger!
MA: How embarrassing! When did you realize it wasn't Sue?
2
F: I thought I'd lost my wallet this morning. But I'd actually left it on the table at a café and some kind person handed it in.
MA: That was lucky.
3
F: I feel really bad. Jeff asked me if he could borrow my camera and I said 'no'. The thing is he's really clumsy and it's a £600 camera.
MA: Don't worry about it. I think I would have done the same thing.
4
F: We had some people round to dinner last night and we spent so long chatting that I forgot to turn the oven off, and all the food I had prepared was completely ruined. It was all dry and burned.
MA: What a nightmare! What did you do?
5
F: My credit card got stuck in the cash machine. I phoned the bank and cancelled the card, and also left a note with my phone number in case someone managed to get it out.
MA: That was good thinking.

Unit 3

21

There's a group of philanthropists in the US – Gates, Buffett, Rockefeller, etcetera – who have contributed a lot of money to good causes over the last fifteen years. The problem for them is that because they're so rich and powerful, people get suspicious of their motives. So when they meet up, they often do so secretly, like they did a few years ago in Manhattan.

22

P = Presenter, D = Didier Bertrand
P: And I'm here with Didier Bertrand from the Research Department of GNH electricity company and today we're talking about 'smart homes' of the future. Everyone has heard about this type of technology in one form or another – robots that clean the house, cookers which will be making our meals for us – and, in a few years, I'm sure we will have heard a lot more. But what we'd all like to know is firstly, what technology is actually just around the corner – not just some techie's or researcher's pipe dream – and secondly, what things are actually practical and useful, and what are just gimmicks. So, first of all, welcome, Didier.
D: Hello.
P: Let's talk about what gadgets our homes will have and I'd like you to tell me if these are a reality, a possibility or just science fiction.
D: OK.
P: 'Intelligent' fridges.
D: Yes, intelligent kitchen gadgets and appliances are here already, but intelligent fridges are only in a few richer homes. I think we'll all be using them when food producers make the packaging intelligent too – so that the fridge can tell you when your food is going bad.
P: So, a reality then, that one. What about ultrasonic showers?
D: Well, the need is already here. In the next ten years or so, water shortages will have become a big problem, so we need to find alternatives. And we already know that sound waves are very effective at cleaning, but whether they're safe or not for humans remains to be proven. Ultrasound is certainly something we will be looking at, but ...
P: A possibility then?
D: A remote one, I think, but a possibility, yes. There's another thing we are working on with sound.
P: What's that?
D: It's sound-proofing using energy fields. At the moment, if you want to sound-proof a room, you use insulation, but in the future people will be using energy fields that isolate a particular space from the rest of the house. So you'll be able to play music as loudly as you want in one room without disturbing anyone else.
P: That sounds amazing. What about surfaces in the house that are intelligent?
D: Yes, that's a very interesting area. We're working on several things – for example, kitchen surfaces that transmit heat – so that when you put a frozen pizza down in a certain smart, or intelligent, packaging, it'll defrost automatically. I don't think people will be cleaning kitchen surfaces either in the future – they'll be self-cleaning. And another area of development – we'll soon be installing walls and surfaces in each room that can act as computer or TV screens so that you can move around the house to do your computing or to watch TV.
P: That technology is quite real, then?
D: Yes, I think in ten years or so, that kind of technology will have become quite common in new-build houses.
P: Wow! Anything else we haven't mentioned?
D: I think people will be able to control light much more intelligently. Our company will be launching a new system for bedrooms next year that simulates the sunrise.
P: I see, so you wake up gradually as the sun comes up, gets brighter.
D: Exactly.

23

1 The weekday edition of *The New York Times* contains more information than the average person in 17th-century England learned in a lifetime.
2 Around a thousand books are published internationally every day and the total of all printed knowledge doubles every five years.
3 More information has been published in the last thirty years than in the previous 5,000.

24

In 2007, the number of people dying from drinking unclean water was a shocking 6,000 per day. Diarrhoea is one of the biggest killers of children in the developing world, a situation that can be changed through the use of vaccines and the drinking of clean water. An ingenious invention, the Lifestraw, may be one answer.

Developed by the non-profit making organization Vestergaard Frandsen, based in Switzerland, this simple device has won a number of awards including *Time Magazine's* Best Innovation of the Year.

Like all good inventions, Lifestraw works on a very simple principle. Water is sucked by the user through a filter that traps 99.9% of all water-borne bacteria, including salmonella and E. coli. As a result, it provides protection against the killer diseases cholera and typhoid, as well as common stomach infections like dysentery and diarrhoea.

The filter contains a substance called PuroTech Disinfecting Resin, or PDR, a material which kills bacteria on contact. Pre-filters made of textile fabric first remove particles up to 15 microns. Each filter lasts up to a year, and has a cleaning capacity of 700 litres of water. This equates to a typical daily intake of two litres of water per day. Lifestraw is only 30 cm long and, being made of plastic, it weighs very little, so it can be worn around the neck without any discomfort to the wearer. Each device costs around US $6.

What are the limitations of Lifestraw? Not many it seems. It shouldn't be shared by users, of course. It isn't effective at filtering out metals such as iron and arsenic. And if you use it with salt water, you will reduce its life by about half. And people who are sensitive or allergic to iodine should seek advice before they use it. Other than that, there are only positives, the main one being that it doesn't run on electrical power but works simply through the mechanical action of sucking. There are some tips for making it work better, for example, by sucking very steadily on the straw, or by periodically blowing some air and water back through it to clean out the filters, but basically it's obvious how it works.

Lifestraw was used successfully in the Haiti earthquake disaster of 2010 and the Pakistan floods of the same year. Like all ideas – particularly those aimed at solving humanitarian problems – it has its sceptics. The charity WaterAid said that while in principle it was a great idea, it did not solve the fundamental problem of access to water for many people in developing countries, which was one of distance, not cleanliness – many people have to walk up to 30 kilometres a day to get water.

27

G = Guest, R = Receptionist

Conversation 1
G: Hello, I wonder if you can help me. I'm a bit worried about the fan in my room. It doesn't look very safe.
R: Sorry, do you mean the ceiling fan or the desk fan?
G: The ceiling fan.

R: What seems to be the problem? Isn't it working?
G: Oh no, it's working OK. But I think it may be loose, because as it goes round, it's moving a lot from side to side. It looks like it's going to come off – and it's directly over my bed.
R: Don't worry. They're supposed to move around like that. It won't come off. But if it makes you feel uncomfortable, you can turn it off and use the desk fan. There's one in the cupboard.
G: Yes, perhaps I'll do that. Thanks.

Conversation 2
G: Hi, can you help me? I can't get the TV in my room to work whatever button I press on the remote control. Perhaps it's me, but the screen just stays blank.
R: Have you tried switching the monitor on separately? There's an on/off button at the front.
G: No, I didn't see that. I'll give that a try.

29

F = Friend, MA = Model answer
1
F: Can you help me?
MA: Sure, if I can.
2
F: Well, I'm having trouble with my computer.
MA: What seems to be the problem with it?
3
F: Well, I was working on it and suddenly the screen went completely blank. Now I can't get it to do anything.
MA: Have you checked the plug? Perhaps you've switched it off by mistake.
4
F: No, it has power. At least, I think so. The light by the power button is still on.
MA: Have you tried switching it off and on again?
5
F: No, OK, good idea. I'll give that a try.
MA: OK. Let me know if it doesn't work. Then I'll come and have a look.

Unit 4

30

P = Presenter, H = Handy, G = Guy Francis
P: Welcome to the *Topical Hour*. In the second part of the programme, we'll be looking at the question of the long-term unemployed. Is each case different or are there measures we can take that will help all unemployed people get back to work? But first, following the news that the graffiti artist 'Tox' has been convicted of vandalism for his graffiti, we ask: 'When is graffiti art and when is it vandalism?' I'm joined by Guy Francis, former arts correspondent for the *Daily News*, and Handy, a graffiti artist himself. So, both are experts in their own way on the subject. First of all, Handy, what was your reaction to this conviction?
H: I thought it was outrageous – he's gone to prison for his art. How can you say that one graffiti artist's work is vandalism and another's is art? Would you let the courts decide what artwork deserved to be shown in a gallery and what didn't? Of course not. There's no difference in this case.
P: Handy's right, isn't he? Graffiti is either art or vandalism. You can't have it both ways. Guy Francis.
G: Well, that's true, if the graffiti is in a place where the owner agrees to have it there. If Tox had put his work in a gallery, as Handy just suggested, there wouldn't have been any trouble. The fact is, he put his name all over public and private property. Every

owner of that property complained and said that their property had been vandalized. In other words, Tox had caused criminal damage. People classed it as damage because all Tox does is to write his name and the year in numbers on the property over and over again. There are no imaginative images at all.

P: So, you're saying that if the owner of a property likes the work that a graffiti artist puts on his wall, then it's art.

G: Well, I'm saying in that case it's not vandalism. The whole debate of whether it's art or not is a different matter. If you take a famous and well-loved graffiti artist like Banksy, whose work sells for tens of thousands of pounds, you can't imagine the owner of a property complaining if some of Banksy's work appeared on his wall. Either type of graffiti could be considered art – but in the eyes of the law, whether or not it's vandalism is up to the owner.

31

1 The message was clear: is this how far we have come since the Stone Age?
2 Often it carries a political or social message, but in an amusing way that ordinary people can relate to.
3 Despite not calling himself an artist, his work has been shown in galleries and has sold for thousands of dollars.
4 Banksy, who is based in the UK, is perhaps the world's best-known graffiti artist.
5 Banksy loves to surprise. In 2005, a picture showing a primitive human being pushing a shopping cart appeared in the British Museum.

33

Speaker 1
You see, there are some places that have a strong tradition of a particular kind of music that, if you were born there, you just can't disassociate yourself from, wherever else in the world you may go. I was born in Mississippi and brought up on country music. Country music tells stories about real life: about love, pain, family, fortune and misfortune. Those are things that everyday folk can relate to and I think it's one of the last genres of music that's in touch with human feelings in that way. It's not just about money and having a good time (though of course that comes into it sometimes), or about politics. It's not insulting or angry in the way that rap music can be. It's about home.

Speaker 2
I think music often plays a more significant role in the culture of poorer communities. When you live in an area which is poor and deprived, you have to get your fun cheap. Music and dance can do that. That's why in Brazil dance music is such an important part of our culture. It's also to do with our history. There are so many different ethnic groups in Brazil that we have a big range of musical influences to draw on: local Indian instruments which are still used today, African rhythms, the melancholy songs of the Portuguese settlers. They've come together to create unique styles of music like samba, carimbó, bossa nova, maracatu. That mixture also brings people together. That's the power music has. You can see that so clearly at Carnaval.

Speaker 3
You don't have to be able to sing or play music to express your feelings through it. Millions of teenagers have been able to express their feelings of frustration at not being understood, or of boredom or anger, or of wanting to break free from the pressures of school and home, by listening to rock music. They hear the very same sentiments they're feeling expressed in lyrics that are supported by a compelling tune or beat. I was brought up with punk rock, which was a kind of do-it-yourself, non-commercial, fast rock music. The music was saying, 'We reject all this commercial packaged stuff you're trying to sell us. Let's just keep the music simple and honest.' And it hit a chord with us, for sure.

Speaker 4
I love hip-hop. I love that it came from just ordinary, average people who wanted to make a better life for themselves from music. I love the innovative side of it too: that people figured out how to make new sounds using old technology – and some new technology too – but they took limited resources and came up with something totally new. No one ever demanded that hip-hop was played on radio or at clubs; there were no restrictions on what it could do or say. Forget the commercial version of hip-hop you hear today – 'cos it doesn't count for anything – the original hip-hop meant living free in an urban environment.

34

I = Ian, S = Sue
I: Hey, Sue, did you see that brilliant documentary on TV last night?
S: No. What was it about?
I: It was about the Amazon.
S: Oh, a nature documentary – not really my kind of thing, actually. I know I should take more of an interest, but I never feel particularly inspired by them. So what was so good about it?
I: Well, I'm a big fan of the presenter, Bruce Parry – you must have seen him, he's been on TV a lot recently. Well, he travels the length of the Amazon interviewing different people who live and work around the river – so not just the indigenous tribes that have lived there for centuries, but also more recent settlers, like loggers and farmers.
S: Yes, I know Bruce Parry. He did that *Tribe* series where he went to live with different tribes in Africa and places. It got on my nerves a bit actually.
I: How can you say that? I have a lot of time for Bruce Parry. I could listen to him all day! Anyway, what I liked about this documentary was that he listened to everyone's side of the story – even the loggers who are tearing down the Amazon Forest. He doesn't make any judgements – the viewer is just left to make up their own mind.
S: Well, it sounds quite good. I guess I just get a bit tired of people making these programmes supposedly about other people living in difficult conditions, but more often it's just about them.

36

F = Friend, MA = Model answer
1
F: What do you think of mobile phones with loud music ringtones?
MA: They really get on my nerves, especially when one starts ringing on the train or bus.
2
F: Do you like graffiti?
MA: I'm not particularly keen on graffiti, but I've seen a few pieces that I like.
3
F: Do you like going to musicals?
MA: Yes, I love going to the theatre, but I don't get many opportunities.
4
F: What's your favourite TV programme?
MA: I'm really into watching sports. I'm a big fan of Formula One racing.
5
F: What kind of music do you listen to? Rock or something else?
MA: No, rock music isn't really my kind of thing. I'm into country and western music.

Unit 5

🎧 37

If you visit the famous French Quarter in New Orleans – which, after the airport, is probably the only part that most tourists see – everything now seems to be back to normal. That's because the French Quarter was largely spared when Hurricane Katrina hit in 2005. There was some damage, but it was fairly quickly repaired. But if you go to one of the residential areas south-east of the centre, it's a different story: you keep on seeing the effects of the disaster, even this long after the storm. There are a lot of homes and neighbourhoods which still have to be rebuilt. It wasn't the winds that did the damage, but rather the flood waters when the city's levees failed to hold the big tidal wave back. Huge numbers of people were forced to leave. A few people decided to resettle elsewhere, but most New Orleanians would never consider leaving their beloved city. About two-thirds of the residents have managed to return and little by little they are rebuilding the city.

The redevelopment plan has not been systematic or co-ordinated. There are some federal projects, some state projects, volunteer groups and also projects run by private benefactors. A particularly interesting project is taking place down in the Lower 9th Ward, an area that was pretty depressed even before the storm. A well-known film actor used his own money to create a non-profit organization called 'Make it right'. Using architects from all over America, they planned to build 150 safe and environmentally-friendly homes in the area where ordinary local people could afford to buy or rent.

All the houses contain innovative design and safety features, because no one wants to see their home flood again. One solution is the 'float house' – the base of the house can rise on two guide posts and act as a raft in case of floods.

I visited some of them myself and was impressed by the imaginativeness of the architecture. At the same time, you can't help wondering how many more homes could have been built if they had used simpler designs and materials. It's a difficult issue. Here's someone genuinely trying to help people rebuild their lives, but is their vision too ambitious? Some critics think it's impractical.

🎧 38

The fact that most people have returned says a lot about how special this city is. The people who live here can't imagine living anywhere else.

I'm a musician and making a living in New Orleans has always been a challenge. We hoped to see more investment in jobs and tourism after the hurricane.

But since Hurricane Katrina, life has definitely become harder. I love this city, but these days, I'm forced to go out of town to find work.

🎧 39

China – minor	placed – taste
found – drowned	rule – tool
front – hunt	way – weigh
meant – sent	whale – they'll
ocean – motion	where – share

🎧 40

N = Newsreader, KR = Kate Rashford
N: A book just published says that exposing infants to complicated words and rich language in the first three years of their lives is key to their later development. According to Dana Suskind of the University of Chicago, who has written the book, hearing rich language not only improves children's language ability but also their overall development and success. Kate Rashford reports.

KR: Dana Suskind's new book, *Thirty Million Words: Building a Child's Brain*, argues that the language we use with children has a huge influence on their development and achievements in later life. This, she says, is because exposure to language – and preferably more than one language – improves a child's IQ and thinking abilities, helping them with other aspects of learning such as spatial awareness.

She summarizes how adults can help infants to develop with what she calls the four 'T's: Tune in, Talk more, Take turns and Turn off the technology. 'Tune in' means that whatever you are doing with your child – taking a bus with them to go shopping, changing their nappy or just doing the housework while they are playing – you must always show interest in what the child is interested in. 'Talk more' means just that. Suskind suggests keeping up a kind of commentary on your child's day and using richer language – not baby talk – to do it. 'Take turns' is her most important rule. It means seeing the child as a true conversation partner. Most adults don't realize they can have a conversation with an infant or a newborn baby, says Suskind. But babies are responding to what you say to them with noises and facial expressions long before they can use their first word.

The fourth T is: Turn off the technology. According to Suskind, the key things for development are interacting and empathy – understanding what the other person is feeling. Empathy is not something you get from digital media – the TV, the iPhone or iPad – even if you are supposed to be learning something. These media may dominate our lives, says Suskind, but we mustn't let them dominate our children's lives.

The inspiration for the title of the book, *Thirty Million Words*, came from some research done at the University of Kansas, which showed that by three years of age, children from lower income backgrounds had on average heard in their lives thirty million fewer words than children from richer backgrounds. And this affected their life chances. It's a powerful statistic and Suskind hopes that making it the title of her new book will help convey her message more strongly.

🎧 43

Conversation 1
A = Alex, B = Barbara
A: Do you know, I find it incredible that in a big city like this there aren't more leisure facilities and green spaces. We've got one ancient swimming pool, a couple of tennis courts and a few children's playgrounds.
B: I know and I agree completely. I think we should try and get a letter signed by as many people as possible asking the council to do something about it.
A: The thing is, it's our taxes they're spending.
B: Yes, absolutely, so we really ought to have a say in how the money is spent, and I think leisure facilities should be a priority.

Conversation 2
B: Have you seen the plans to reduce traffic in the centre of town? They look awful. I think they should just make the whole centre a pedestrian area. For me, that would make much more sense.
A: Well, I understand why you say that and I used to think the same. But actually, you also need to consider all the old people who depend on buses and public transport. I'm more concerned that they just wouldn't be able to come into the town centre and use local shops anymore if vehicles were banned.
B: Not necessarily. It seems to work in other city centres.

F = Friend, MA = Model answer

1
F: I find it amazing that no one has developed the area around the canal. It has such potential.
MA: I agree. It's an obvious area for development. What they should do is make a nice area with shops and restaurants.

2
F: I think that more money should be invested in leisure facilities for young people in the area.
MA: Absolutely. There's not enough for young people to do.

3
F: The trouble with having a business park out of town is that it encourages people to drive to work. What do you think?
MA: I know what you mean. But for me, it's better than people driving into the city centre.

4
F: Do you think the council should make the city centre a pedestrian area?
MA: I think that depends on what they plan to do about public transport.

5
F: Have you seen the new shopping centre they're building in the centre of town? It's horrible.
MA: I don't mind the design. I'm more concerned about what will happen to the local shops.

Unit 6

🔘 **46**

Speaker 1
Let's not pretend that just by staying at home, you're going to relax and switch off. If you're going to get a real break, you need to make a few rules and changes – a few don'ts, if you like. Tell your work that you are going away and you can't be contacted. Don't answer the phone – switch on the answer phone and listen to messages once a day to check that nothing urgent has come in. Change the weekly routine: you don't have to do a weekly shop, for example. Instead, make food shopping something that's fun and nice to do. Shop when you need to; go to the deli, the farmer's market and so on. Don't watch the same old TV programme that you watch each week. Don't do the cleaning – get a cleaner. I don't want to sound prescriptive, but unless you make some rules, you just won't relax properly.

Speaker 2
My idea of a staycation is to pamper myself for a week. I call it my 'home spa week'. I get up late. I go for a walk or a short run, and then I have a massage each day at the local health club. It would be easier not to do things to keep fit, but actually it makes me feel fantastic for the rest of the day. Then I take a late lunch – down by the waterfront usually – and spend the rest of the afternoon reading. Some evenings I spend the time preparing a meal very carefully; other times I go out to a show. I don't think it's extravagant, because I know whatever I do, I'm spending less than I would be if I went away on holiday.

Speaker 3
We had a staycation last year and I just organized loads of exciting things for the family to do every day. I hope I didn't overdo it. I think they enjoyed it. I'm just not one of those people who likes to sit still and do nothing when I'm on holiday. So we went to two theme parks; we went mountain biking in the Brecon hills; we even camped out in the garden one night. I think holidays are all about experiences and we certainly had some of those. We got lost on our bikes one day for about four hours. I tried not to let the children know that I was worried, but I was! Luckily we found the track again before it got dark.

Speaker 4
My advice for a staycation is just to keep it simple. It's an opportunity to enjoy the basic things in life and what nature has to offer. So you really mustn't let modern life dictate what you do too much. Do things with the family – take walks together, make meals for each other, play family games or just chat in the evenings – and don't get involved with anything even vaguely electronic, like computer games or the TV.

🔘 **47**

1 In tough economic times, people will try not to spend so much on luxuries and that includes holidays.
2 However, they don't want to go without a holiday altogether, because holidays are an important break from the stresses of work and daily life.
3 You don't have to go abroad to go on holiday. You can have a staycation instead. These have increased in popularity in recent years.
4 I don't think it's a bad trend because it means that people discover more about their own country, and at the same time, they boost the local economy.

🔘 **49**

A first look at the *National Geographic Endeavour II* does not make you think 'cruise ship'. It isn't painted white and there are none of the sleek lines of a modern luxury cruise liner. That's because the *Endeavour* is actually a ship that started life as a fishing trawler in the 1960s, working in the waters of the North Sea and North Atlantic.

They say 'Don't judge a book by its cover', but in some senses, the *Endeavour* still *is* a working ship, because it has to combine the qualities of a comfortable passenger boat with those of a working expedition ship. So on its decks you will find a small swimming pool and a sun deck, but there are also small cranes for lowering kayaks or Zodiacs – small rubber inflatable boats – into the water. You won't find luxuries such as a casino, a hairdresser or room service, but there is a library, a fitness centre and a relaxing lounge.

The *Endeavour* used to run expeditions from the Arctic to Antarctica, but these days it's to be found mostly in calmer waters around the Galápagos Islands. The ship is used as a base from which passengers can take trips by kayak or Zodiac to explore the islands.

Photographers and expert naturalist guides from National Geographic accompany the passengers, giving advice on how to take amazing pictures and teaching them about the nature on these unique islands. It's educational and exciting at the same time. In one excursion, you can follow a path through tide pools and underwater caves in search of seals, sea lions and marine iguanas. In another, you can snorkel near a coral reef and swim among the tropical fish, or even, if you're lucky, with Galápagos penguins or dolphins.

The trips are not cheap, working out at around $1,000 dollars a day, but these are not ordinary holidays: for your money you get to visit one of the most remote regions on Earth, the benefit of expert knowledge, reasonable comfort, good Ecuadorian food and a real sense of adventure.

🎵 50

J = Joe, S = Steve

J: Hey, Steve. It's Joe. I'm just calling to say I'll be coming in on the five o'clock train this evening.

S: Fantastic. But I can't pick you up, I'm afraid. I'll be working then.

J: That's OK. I'll just make my way over to you at home – if that's all right.

S: Well, you could do that, but alternatively, since it's going to be a nice evening, why don't we meet up in town – say at Sara's Café down by the seafront?

J: Yeah, all right. That sounds nice. How do I get to Sara's Café?

S: Just hop on any bus from the station and ask the driver for King's Street.

J: OK.

S: Look out for the pier and get off there. Then walk down the front towards the city centre and you'll see the café on your right.

J: OK. If I get held up, I'll call you.

S: Actually, why don't you come and meet me at my office first? It's just as easy.

J: OK, where's that?

S: Well, get off at the same stop and walk in the same direction but turn down Ship Street. Call me when you get there and I'll come out and meet you.

🎵 51

1 I'd prefer to drive, but the car is behaving strangely.
2 It's not difficult to find, but it's quite a long way from the station.
3 I could come and meet you, but I don't finish work until 6.00 p.m.
4 The bus is cheap, but it makes a lot of stops on the way.
5 You could take a taxi, but it's a very scenic walk.

🎵 52

F = Friend, MA = Model answer

1

F: Hi there. I'm coming in on the train tomorrow at two o'clock. What's the best way to get to your house from there?

MA: The easiest thing is to take the bus.

2

F: OK. Is it far?

MA: No, it's only a ten-minute ride.

3

F: Great and how do I know when it's my stop?

MA: Look out for the big shoe factory on your left and it's the next stop after that.

4

F: OK, and what do I do when I get off the bus?

MA: Walk along the road until you see Harbord Road on your left. Turn down there.

5

F: Shall I call you when I get there?

MA: That's a good idea. Then I'll come out and meet you.

6

F: Great. Look, if I get held up, I'll call you. Otherwise, look forward to seeing you tomorrow.

MA: Yes, me too. Have a good trip.

Unit 7

🎵 53

Speaker 1

People who are in favour of teaching your children at home generally argue that the local schools don't stretch children enough, or that they don't recognize their child's individual needs. I'm sure these people mean well, but I think they're missing the point. Interaction with other children from a range of backgrounds – not just your own brothers and sisters – is a key part of learning and you just don't get that if you're stuck in your own house all day.

Speaker 2

Parents often discipline their children for fighting or being unkind to each other, but there's new evidence to suggest that this kind of behaviour may not be a bad thing. Psychologists say that by competing in this way, children are learning valuable social skills. It's common for brothers and sisters to squabble over toys or to compete for attention. They will even continue to do this later in life – fight for their parents' approval, that is – but generally they find a way of working it out so that no one's hurt. That type of negotiation in relationships is important training for later life.

Speaker 3

Where you are in the family clearly has an influence on your behaviour more generally. We're all familiar with eldest children who are organizing and bossy types and middle children who feel ignored. Being the baby of our family, I'm particularly interested in youngest child syndrome. Certainly you have to fight more for attention – that's why younger children are often the clowns of the family. Parents tend to let you get away with things that your brothers and sisters didn't. You also have the advantage of learning from your older siblings ... and their mistakes.

Speaker 4

I think far too much attention is paid to how parents should bring up children and far too little to how much other environmental factors affect them. Have you ever watched a two-year-old when another slightly older child comes into the room? They're fascinated. They watch what they do, they try to join in – much more than with an adult. What's more, the elder child will quickly take on the role of teacher or parent, explaining pictures in a book, for example, 'Look. That's a lion! Can you say "lion"?' In a lot of societies, it's quite normal in large families just to leave the children to get on with it. I think parents in the West should do that instead of intervening so much.

🎵 54

Everything depends on what you see as the future role of your children. In other words, what is it that you are raising them to do?

Do you want them to be good members of society? If so, you will teach them values such as obeying the law, co-operating with others and generally being good citizens.

Or do you want them to be successful individuals? If so, you will help them to be free thinkers and to be independent.

Or is it important that they are good family members? Then you will teach them to respect their elders and to follow family traditions.

🎵 56

/uː/: blue, fortune, lunar, rude, suit, truce
/juː/: consume, humanity, humour, menu, used, usually

57

Desmond Morris trained originally as a zoologist and in that capacity, he observed the behaviour of many different species of animals. However, his lifelong interest has been human rather than animal behaviour, and unlike the traditional experts in human behaviour – the psychologist, the sociologist and the anthropologist – he is not so interested in what people say, but rather in what they do. In fact, he gives little attention to human speech because he feels that human actions tell us far more about people than anything they might say. Indeed, it is said that in human communication, as much as ninety per cent is non-verbal.

In an interview given some years ago on BBC's Radio 4, Morris gave a fascinating example of this. The non-verbal communication that he described was called 'postural echo' and this is how he explained it. Morris and the presenter were sitting discussing Morris's work in a radio studio. They were both sitting down facing each other across a table. Both had one forearm resting on the table and the other forearm upright with their chin resting on one hand. Both were leaning forward interestedly as they talked to each other. They had adopted what Morris called postural echo: that is to say, because they had a common interest, they were imitating each other's posture. This particular posture I've just described is typical when people are showing interest in what they are hearing.

In another situation, though, such postural echo might be totally inappropriate. The example Morris gave was that of a job interview. Imagine you are being interviewed for a job and the boss who is interviewing you sits back in his chair and puts his feet up on a stool. His posture is showing that he is in a relaxed and dominant position. Your posture, on the other hand, should show that you are in a subordinate position: in other words, you should be sitting upright, perhaps leaning forward a little to show interest, with your hands on your lap. If you were to echo his posture, it would send the message that you felt as relaxed as him and he is not hiring another boss – he is looking for a subordinate. At best, you would not get the job; at worst, the boss would find it deeply insulting and end the interview immediately.

59

Dowry-giving, the gift of money from one family to another on the occasion of a marriage, is still common in certain parts of the world. It symbolizes different things. For example, it can be a sign of wealth and increase social status. It can have a historical and practical meaning: as a rule, in the past, brides did not go out to work, so this was her financial contribution to the marriage. It's customary for a dowry to be given by the bride's family to the groom's family, but it can work the other way around, as in Nigeria, where a small dowry is given by the groom's family.

The engagement ceremony in Nigeria marks the beginning of the wedding celebrations and is an occasion for people to celebrate and have fun before the official ceremony, and also to give gifts to the couple. It takes place on the evening or a couple of nights before the wedding itself. During the party, there's a lot of music, often played by a live band, and dancing. It used to be traditional for money to be thrown at the couple's feet while they danced, but now people usually bring regular wedding gifts. After the party, the groom's family delivers a kind of dowry to the bride's family's house in the form of a gift of traditional clothes and jewellery. It's not the last time the groom has to visit the bride's house. On the night of the wedding, after the reception party is finished, the bride goes back to her own house where she waits until she's claimed by the groom and taken to their new home.

61

F = Friend, MA = Model answer

1
F: What does the groom wear on his wedding day?
MA: It's traditional for the groom to wear a morning suit and a top hat, but these days, he can also wear an ordinary suit.

2
F: What symbolic acts are there at the ceremony?
MA: The bride arrives with her father and he then gives her hand to the groom. That symbolizes the handing over of his responsibility for her to the groom.

3
F: What happens after the wedding ceremony?
MA: The bride and groom go to a reception, usually in a special car, where they have a big party with all their friends and family.

4
F: What kinds of gifts are given?
MA: Usually people give the couple things that will be useful in their new home: kitchen equipment and so on.

5
F: Is special music played at the reception?
MA: Not really. Once the bride and groom have had their first dance together, everyone usually dances to pop music.

Unit 8

62

Speaker 1
Rhea: I spent most of my life working for a big insurance company in the UK, which is where I come from. I felt I had achieved a lot of things in my life – got a good job, brought up a family – but I wanted something more, something with real significance. I felt that insurance was just a money-making business and I wanted to help people in a more meaningful way. Particularly I wanted to help children get a good education. I was very fortunate because a friend told me about a volunteer programme in Rwanda in Africa. The aim of the programme was to teach nursery school teachers the value of learning through play. In many countries, playing is seen as not useful – basically, people don't see it as learning. So I was trained by the voluntary organization and then I went out to a small village in Rwanda to work with local teachers. The school was in a terrible condition and the kids sat at desks all day and there was no room to do anything else. But our methods have been a great success. The children love coming to school, they seem more interested, and the teachers are really motivated by the new methods. And for me, I have found my calling, something that really stimulates me – helping to educate people who really need and want to learn.

Speaker 2
Sasha: When I left art college seven years ago, I didn't really have any illusions about how difficult it would be to make a living from my art. I knew it would be hard so I imagined that art would pretty much be my hobby unless I got lucky. My ambition was not so much to be a professional artist, but just to work in the art world. I moved to Glasgow in Scotland with a couple of friends, who were also artists, because basically it was cheaper to live there than in London, where I'm from. We found a flat and also a space in an old warehouse that had been used for storing sugar which we could use as a studio. But I only went there in my spare time. For work, I did odd jobs

like being a waiter and working in bars. Then one of my friends had the idea of setting up a gallery. So we turned the warehouse space into a gallery – it was a lot of work – and then we got artists from the local art school to exhibit there. Pretty soon, we started to get noticed. We had good reviews in local newspapers and even one art magazine. Then we attracted one or two more well-known artists to exhibit their work there. And it just took off from there – it's going incredibly well. I'm still enjoying painting in my free time – a lot, actually – but I feel that in helping to run a gallery, I've found a job where I can be with the people and the things I love anyway.

64
1 match   2 ship   3 chew   4 Swiss   5 shock   6 bass

65
I am very suspicious of bucket lists now. They started out as a good idea, but like a lot of things they have become too commercial. In bookshops you now find titles like *100 Places You Must Visit Before You Die* or *100 Films You Should See*. And if your dream is to hold a baby tiger, there are even websites you can go on where they can make your wish come true.

66
Speaker 1
In the 1970s, Cancún was just a small fishing village – a few huts on the edge of a mangrove forest. Today that forest is buried and rotting underneath 500 hotels. Only a few inhabitants remember the forest and the seven million tourists that visit each year don't know it ever existed. This place is a classic example of how not to build a tourist resort. Nature is for sale here. The mangroves are not the only victims. The coral reef all along the coast is also slowly being destroyed by all the tourists' pollution. Very little waste water is treated: it's either pumped into the sea or injected into the land, from where in time it returns to the surface. Up to now, conservationists have failed to stop this development or the pollution it's caused.

Speaker 2
The story of the West African giraffe is a conservation success story. A heroic effort on the part of conservationists has saved the giraffe from extinction – from numbers as low as fifty giraffes twenty years ago to over 200 today. The main job was to track the giraffe's movements, since they travel huge distances looking for food. This was done by fitting them with GPS satellite collars – easy with their long necks, you'd think, but actually it's a delicate operation because the giraffes have to be anaesthetized first. Once they knew where the giraffes were going, the conservationists could then begin to educate local people about the dangers facing these wonderful creatures, and to compensate farmers when their land had been damaged by them.

Speaker 3
If you mention the term 'conservation efforts', people tend to think of attempts to save endangered animals, like the tiger; or to protect poor communities from big corporate organizations who are trying to use their land. But in fact, many conservation efforts are small in scale and many have positive outcomes. I'll give you an example: the black poplar tree in Britain. The black poplar is one of Britain's rarest species of tree and its numbers have been declining for decades. That's because much of its natural habitat – the floodplain – has been built on with new housing. Less floodplain means less protection against flooding. So conservationists persuaded local authorities to stop building on the floodplain and reintroduce the trees. As a result, black poplar numbers are rising again.

67
A: So, how are we going to divide these tasks up? Basically, there's the decoration of the main tent to do; there's the hi-fi equipment to fetch from the shop and then that needs to be set up; and there's a bit of food to prepare.
B: Oh, I'd rather not do any cooking.
A: It's not cooking, it's just cutting up some pizza and putting out a few crisps and things. But if you'd prefer to do something else, as I say, there are plenty of other things.
B: No, I'll do that.
A: OK. And what about you, Carla?
C: Well, I don't mind helping with the decorations.
A: Great. And could you help out with that too, Harry?
H: I could, but I'd rather someone else did that. I'm not very good at that kind of thing. It'd probably be better if I went to get the hi-fi equipment.
A: OK, and I like doing the decorations anyway, so that's perfect. Let's get on with it then.

68
1   Would you prefer a proper meal or just something light?
2   Shall we take a short break?
3   Would you rather we went to the film another night?
4   Do you like Manchester more than London?

69
F = Friend, MA = Model answer
1
F: I'm going to ask you to explain your preferences for certain things. Ready? Here we go: bath or shower?
MA: I prefer having a shower, generally. It's quicker and more refreshing.
2
F: Drive or be driven?
MA: I'd rather drive. I feel more in control.
3
F: Tea or coffee?
MA: I like coffee more in the mornings and tea in the afternoon.
4
F: Morning or afternoon?
MA: I prefer the morning to the afternoon. It takes me a little while to wake up, but I generally feel fresher in the morning.
5
F: Smart or casual clothes?
MA: I'd rather wear casual clothes, even at work. It just feels more comfortable.
6
F: Eating in or eating out?
MA: Actually, I prefer eating in, but I'd rather someone else did the cooking!

72
If you mention the term 'conservation efforts', people tend to think of attempts to save endangered animals, like the tiger; or to protect poor communities from big corporate organizations who are trying to use their land. But in fact, many conservation efforts are small in scale and many have positive outcomes.

Unit 9

73
P = Presenter, J = Journalist
P: … that's just one aspect of photojournalism. The question I'd really like to put to you is: When is altering a photo OK and when is it not?
J: Well, that's a good question. In 1982, *National Geographic Magazine* published on its cover a photo of the pyramids

in Egypt. In order to fit the tops of the two pyramids onto its cover, photo editors digitally decreased the space between them. People said that this was a manipulation of reality and was wrong. Several years later, an associate editor defended the action. He said that although the magazine had altered the image, they hadn't done anything wrong. He said that he was opposed in general to manipulation of images, but that the cover was a graphic item, not a photo in a news story. He also said that photo editors had always touched up photos, but that this practice was now becoming more sophisticated with tools like Photoshop and Scitex.

P: So he said it was the fault of modern technology that people were altering images?

J: No. He was saying that the cover of a magazine was more like a piece of advertising, and it had to look aesthetically pleasing to help the magazine sell.

P: You mean the cover has to look good?

J: Yes, that's right. Other editors have used the same argument to alter images for book covers.

P: And what about cases of manipulation in hard news stories – you know, really serious and important ones?

J: That is, of course, a far more serious thing. Again in the 1980s, there was a case with *Picture Week* magazine. The magazine put together two different photos – one of Nancy Reagan, the other of Raisa Gorbachev – put them together in such a way that they appeared to be great friends. This wasn't actually the case and of course people complained, saying that they had been given a false impression.

P: So what's the rule?

J: Well, some people say, 'Don't trust a photo if there's anything important riding on it.' Personally, I think that's going too far. We live now in a world of digitally enhanced visual images and alternative realities. But the public's not stupid – they know that and can make up their own minds about what's real and what's not.

75

1 Like many of his fellow professionals, photographer Fritz Hoffman recommends using an analogue camera.

2 A digital camera encourages you to look at the preview before you take a photo, but an analogue camera keeps you in the moment.

3 Hoffman also claims that with a digital camera you need more time to edit the images after they've been taken.

4 That's so that you can make them look like the image as you saw it.

77

Most broadcasters and news writers are naturally concerned about being fair in their reporting. They don't want to be seen as biased – that is, of seeming in favour of one side of an argument. The solution, they think, is always to present both sides of any argument equally.

So, if a radio station is covering a story about climate change and has an interview with a scientist who claims that human activity has caused global temperatures to rise to dangerous levels, in order to be fair, they will also feature an interview with another scientist or expert who claims that this is nonsense and that the rise in temperature has nothing to do with human activity, but is all part of the Earth's natural cycle of warmer and colder periods. But there's a fundamental problem with this kind of so-called 'fairness', because it leads the listener or reader to think that both arguments have equal weight, when in fact the overwhelming amount of scientific evidence and the overwhelming number of

scientists agree that human activity is responsible for global warming.

Back in the 1970s, reporters used to do something similar when reporting the dangers of smoking. All the evidence pointed to the fact that smoking was harmful to your health and caused various medical conditions, such as heart disease and lung cancer. Yet the broadcasters, in the interests of fairness, would always interview another scientist (very often one who was an employee of a tobacco company) to say that there was no clear evidence to link smoking to such diseases.

Many people, particularly in the scientific community, think that this kind of journalistic 'fairness' often distorts the true facts. They say that anyone who shouts their opinions loudly enough these days is given an equal hearing to those who quietly support their view with scientific facts. The right way to report any debate, it is claimed, is to give a proportionate amount of time to those who support or oppose an idea with real facts. So, in the case of global warming, 99 per cent of the time should be given to presenting the argument that human activity is causing it, and only one per cent to the view that it is part of a natural cycle, because that is the same proportion of scientific evidence that supports each view.

78

A = Annie, J = Jane

J: Hi, Annie.

A: Hi, Jane. Did you hear the good news about Patrick? Guess what?

J: What?

A: Well, you know he was doing a comedy routine ...

J: You mean that show that he and his friends took to the Edinburgh Festival.

A: Yes. Well, apparently he was spotted by someone from a big theatrical agency and they want him to sign a contract with them.

J: Really? Who told you about it?

A: Er ... Kate. She reckons that it won't be long before we see him on TV.

J: Hmm. Well, I'd take that with a pinch of salt if I were you. It could just mean he gets a bit of advertising work or something.

A: No, according to Kate, it's more than that. They talked about him getting acting parts on TV.

J: Really? Well, that'd be fantastic. I heard that it was really difficult to get that kind of work.

A: I think it is, which shows he must have really impressed them. But don't tell anyone just yet. I think he wants to keep quiet about it.

J: Don't worry. I'm not the type to spread gossip. Does the agency take a big fee?

A: It seems that they only take ten or fifteen per cent, supposedly.

J: That sounds all right. Well, that's great news. Thanks for telling me.

80

F = Friend, MA = Model answer

1

F: Did you hear the good news about taxes?

MA: Good news about taxes? No, what happened?

2

F: Apparently, the government is going to reduce taxes for all workers.

MA: Really? That doesn't sound very likely. Who told you that?

3

F: Ben told me. It seems that everyone will only pay half the tax they are paying now.

MA: Half? Hmm ... Take no notice of what Ben says.

4
F: Well, maybe he's blown it a bit out of proportion. He said it will be on the news tonight.
MA: OK. Well, I'll watch the news and see.
5
F: What do you reckon is the truth of it?
MA: I reckon that they've reduced taxes by half a per cent or something and Ben misunderstood.

Unit 10

🎧 81
P = Presenter, M = Marjorie Barakowski
P: Ronald Reagan was raised in a small village in Illinois and he graduated from Eureka College, Illinois with a degree in economics and sociology. He worked for a short time as a radio broadcaster in Iowa, and then moved to Los Angeles to follow a career as an actor in films and television. After joining the Republican Party in 1962, his skills as an orator were noticed and he was persuaded to run for Governor of California. He did a good job as Governor and this led to his nomination for Republican presidential candidate in 1980, which he won. He then went on to become the President of the United States between 1981 and 1989. He took a hard line against communism and his second term of office saw the collapse of the Soviet Union and the beginning of the end of communism in eastern Europe. He was often ridiculed for not being very clever – a second-rate actor, who could only read the lines he was given by his advisors – but he remains one of the most popular American Presidents of the past fifty years. Why? I put that question to political historian Marjorie Barakowski.
M: Ronald Reagan understood the fundamental essence of leadership: that is, that you have to be able to communicate. Reagan always gave the impression that he was listening when he was speaking to you. It was almost as if it didn't matter what his political views were. He made people feel that they mattered. He looked you in the eye, smiled at you, made you feel special. That is a fantastic quality to have.
     I'd also have to say that he presided over a time of great economic growth in America. When he came to power, things weren't great for most Americans and he gave them hope. It obviously helped that the economy thrived during his presidency. But, nevertheless, Reagan's style of communication stands out as a model for all leaders. If you can connect with the ordinary person, there's very little you can do wrong.

🎧 83
1   I guess I was lucky to do a subject that not many other people at college did. I studied plant sciences and after my course, I got a job as a research assistant at the Institute of Botany.
2   It's not easy to be an artist and make a living from it. You're always wondering if it would be better just to get a job with a regular income.
3   I was always told that having good qualifications and the right degree opens doors, but actually it's good communication skills that help you advance in an organization.

🎧 84
In 2016 the US treasury announced that it would put the face of a black woman, Harriet Tubman, on its $20 bill. Unlike former president Andrew Jackson, whose image she has replaced, few people outside the United States have any idea who Harriet Tubman is, nor what she did for her country.

Harriet Tubman was born into slavery in Maryland, USA, around 1820. She had a strange disability, called narcolepsy, which meant she could fall asleep at any time without warning. The disability was the result of being struck on the head by an iron weight, which had been thrown at another slave, but had hit her instead.

In 1851 she used the 'Underground Railroad', a system of secret routes and safe houses, to escape to a neighbouring 'free' state. When she realized she had reached freedom she said she looked at her hands to see if she was still the same person. 'The sun came up like gold through the trees,' she recalled, 'and I felt I was in heaven.'

She spent the rest of the war actively fighting slavery. After finding her own freedom, she started trying to help other slaves to escape – first members of her own family and then others – using the Underground Railroad. She became what was known as a 'conductor', helping to lead almost 300 other slaves to freedom over a fifteen-year period. She was a determined woman – it is said that she threatened to shoot any of the escapees who said they wanted to turn back.

During the civil war between the northern and southern states of America, Harriet Tubman became a spy for the northern forces. Black people were effective as spies because many white southerners did not think they had the intelligence to do such work. Tubman also worked as a nurse in the war and even acted as a military officer, leading a force of 300 free black soldiers to liberate seven hundred slaves in South Carolina.

In spite of her brave service for her country, Tubman never received a pension in later life from the government – she had to survive on her husband's pension. (She was married twice, and had one adopted child.) After the war she wrote her story with the help of a biographer. She also travelled across the eastern United States giving public speeches about her experiences and campaigning for voting rights for women. She died of pneumonia in 1913 and only then received the recognition that her impressive career deserved, when she was given a full military funeral at Auburn cemetery.

🎧 86
Speaker 1
Well, I'd be interested to know a bit more about the job, because although I'm very keen on the idea of working with young people – people are always telling me that I'm very good with children – I actually don't have much direct experience of this age group.

Speaker 2
I specialize in canoeing and various other water sports, but I feel comfortable with most outdoor activities really – as long as you're not going to expect me to lead a climbing expedition up a glacier or anything. I haven't done mountaineering. But I have led groups before, so I've got organizational skills.

Speaker 3
I think I'd be very well suited to this job, actually. Although I haven't led expeditions as such, I've been working as a physical education teacher at my local secondary school for the last four years. I'm good at quite a number of sports, in fact. But when I saw your advertisement, I thought, 'This could be just the thing for me.' I'm familiar with your organization and I really like the fact that you run these activities for kids from poor backgrounds.

🎵 **88**

I = Interviewer, MA = Model answer

1
I: So what did you study at university?
MA: I studied media, but I specialized in newspaper journalism.

2
I: And what attracted you to our newspaper?
MA: I want to follow a career in journalism and I'm very interested in local news.

3
I: How do you feel about working to very strict deadlines?
MA: I think I'm good at working under pressure. I had a lot of experience of that at university.

4
I: Have you had any experience of writing for a newspaper before?
MA: Not really, but I think I write well and I'm very keen to learn.

5
I: If you get the job, don't you think you might become bored just dealing with local news stories?
MA: No. I'm serious about wanting to become a professional journalist and this would be a perfect place to start.

Unit 11

🎵 **89**

Dr K. David Harrison believes that language diversity is just as important as bio-diversity. He's part of a *National Geographic* project called 'Enduring Voices', whose aim is to document languages which are little known and in danger of becoming extinct. It's estimated that over half the world's 7,000 languages will disappear by 2050 and so the race is on to trace and record these languages, and also to help keep them alive.

Diversity doesn't depend on the size of a territory or country. In Bolivia, which only has a population of twelve million, there are 37 different languages, belonging to eighteen language families. This is the same number as the whole of Europe.

Dr Harrison seeks out these language 'hotspots' – places where there is a great diversity of languages spoken and where some are in danger. Studies in the Oklahoma region of the USA succeeded in discovering 26 languages, one of which, Yuchi, had as few as seven speakers. By highlighting this fact, researchers were able to help the community to keep this dying language alive.

Why is this work important? According to Harrison, 'When we lose a language, we lose centuries of human thinking about time, seasons, sea creatures, reindeer, edible flowers, mathematics, landscapes, myths, music – the unknown and the everyday.' Some ancient cultures managed to build large monuments by which we can remember their achievements, but all cultures express their genius through their languages and stories. We would be shocked if the Great Pyramid at Giza disappeared; we should be equally concerned when we lose a language.

These languages store knowledge which can be of huge benefit to people today. The Yupik language is spoken by the Eskimo peoples of Siberia and Alaska. A book written a few years ago by Yupik elders and scientists in which they described the changing conditions of the ice in the Arctic was able to help other scientists to understand how climate change is affecting the polar ice.

One of the original arguments for globalization was that it could bring us all closer together. And in some ways this may be true – but that doesn't mean we all have to do the same thing – eat the same food and speak the same language. If anything, globalization has reminded us how important differences and diversity are. He couldn't save Ubykh – a language spoken near the Black Sea – from extinction, or Kakadu – an Australian aboriginal language, but Harrison and his team aim to save as many languages as they can.

🎵 **90**

1   Examples of two languages that have become extinct this century are Munichi – M-U-N-I-C-H-I – from Peru and Wappo – W-A-P-P-O – from the San Francisco area of the USA.

2   David Harrison is a linguist at Swarthmore College (S-W-A-R-T-H-M-O-R-E) in Pennsylvania (P-E-N-N-S-Y-L-V-A-N-I-A).

3   In 2008, the Enduring Voices project found a new language in Arunchal Pradesh (A-R-U-N-C-H-A-L) in India, called Koro (K-O-R-O).

4   Chary is a word from the Siberian language 'Tofa'. Spelled C-H-A-R-Y, it means a four-year-old domesticated reindeer.

5   The longest non-scientific word in the English language is floccinaucinihilipilification, which means the habit of regarding something as unimportant. I'll spell it: F-L-O-C-C-I-N-A-U-C-I-N-I-H-I-L-I-P-I-L-I-F-I-C-A-T-I-O-N.

🎵 **92**

1   Meg is a border collie, a smart breed of dog used by farmers because they understand instructions well and they like to be helpful. Their usual job is to round up and direct sheep. You can show Meg a picture of a toy and tell her its name (like a duck or a frisbee), then ask her to go and find it in a room full of toys. Once she has found it once and learned the name, all you have to do the next time is to ask her to fetch the duck or the frisbee from the room and she will go and find it.

2   Betty is a New Caledonian crow. These animals are pretty inventive tool makers. In the wild, they use sticks, for example, to get insects out of trees. But what they found in the lab was that these birds were able to make tools from materials that they had never used before. Experimenters placed a piece of meat in a little basket and put it in a tube. Betty looked at the problem, then found a straight piece of wire, bent it into the shape of a hook using her beak and lifted the basket from the tube.

3   Maya is a dolphin. I think most people know that dolphins have incredible imitative abilities. They can see an action performed and then repeat it when ordered to. They also seem to understand spoken directions from humans very well. So you can get two of them to leap out of the water and turn a somersault at the same time. But in fact they do these kinds of synchronized tricks in the wild anyway, because they're naturally playful creatures, but no one really understands how they communicate with each other to get the timing so perfect.

4   Kanzi is a Bonobo monkey who has been taught sign language so that he can communicate with humans. One anecdote about his intelligence is that on a walk in the woods, Kanzi indicated that he wanted marshmallows and a fire. He was given the marshmallows and some matches. He found some twigs, broke them into pieces, built a fire, lit it with the matches and then, most amazingly, toasted the marshmallows on a stick over the fire. Bonobos are known for being expressive and good communicators,

but even experts who study them were surprised by this behaviour.

5   Psychobird is a western scrub-jay. These birds are known for being pretty mischievous – they play tricks all the time. They're also supposed to be the only non-mammals that plan ahead. They hide food that they're storing up for future use in stores or caches. Their large memories allow them to remember as many as 200 such hiding places. In a lab, Psychobird hid food so carefully that none of the experimenters could work out where she had put it.

93
S = Student, L = Lecturer
S: Hi, have you got a minute? I just wanted to ask a bit more about this course.
L: Sure, how can I help?
S: Well, first of all, thanks for the interesting lecture. [L: You're welcome – glad you found it interesting …] but there's quite a lot to take in and I don't really have the same background knowledge as some of the other students.
L: Don't worry – I think a lot of people find it difficult at first. Things will become clearer.
S: Well, can you explain what the course is going to be about, because I thought it was going to be about Roman history mainly?
L: Well, it's a mixture of Greek – mainly Hellenistic – and Roman history.
S: Sorry, I didn't catch that word – Helle-something?
L: Hellenistic – Alexander the Great and so on.
S: Oh, yeah, OK. And are you saying that no previous knowledge of ancient history is needed?
L: Well, a little understanding of the geography of the Eastern Mediterranean is very helpful, and if you've heard or read some Greek myths and legends, it helps too.
S: Sorry, I'm not really with you. You mean stories like the war at Troy and so on?
L: Exactly.
S: OK, well, could you give me an example of a book I could read now, outside class?
L: Um, you could have a look at some texts by Herodotus. He was a historian of the fifth century BC and his histories read more like good bedtime stories!
S: Did you say Herodotus?
L: That's right, H-E-R-O-D-O-T-U-S.
S: OK, thanks. I'll do that.

95
T = Teacher, MA = Model answer
1
T: So you wanted to ask me a question about the exam at the end of this course?
MA: Yes. Can you explain what the exam involves?
2
T: Yes, there's a two-hour written exam and then a short 'viva' afterwards.
MA: Sorry, what do you mean by 'viva'.
3
T: It's a short oral exam to discuss what you have written. They ask you simple questions.
MA: Could you give me an example of the questions?
4
T: Yes, they might ask you to explain your reasons for an argument. But this part only carries a small proportion of the total mark.
MA: Sorry, I'm not really with you.
5
T: What I mean is the viva or oral exam is only fifteen per cent of the total marks.
MA: Did you say fifteen or fifty per cent?

Unit 12

96
How does national character affect economics? Well, let's just consider people's attitude to money at its simplest level. There are basically two types of people – savers and spenders – and we all know people who fit these descriptions. Savers are prudent and careful, never wasteful. Of course they spend money too, but only when they can afford it and only if it's a wise or long-term investment. On the other side, we have the spenders, the more extravagant types. For them, life is too short to worry about saving a little money here or there.

So, can you apply such simple stereotypes on a national scale? During the 2010–2011 global debt crisis, some commentators tried to do exactly that, saying that certain countries had been irresponsible with the money that they had borrowed from banks and governments in more prudent countries. As a result, people in these countries would have to work longer hours, pay more taxes and even accept lower wages if they wanted to receive any more loans.

The question these commentators failed to ask was whether it was irresponsible of the so-called 'prudent countries' to lend the money in the first place. Because when you lend money, you take two risks: you risk perhaps losing the money, but you also risk putting the borrower in a difficult situation. In such a transaction, both parties have a similar motive – to get more money – and so both have a shared responsibility.

To portray one country as a nation of extravagant spenders and another as a nation of prudent savers is too simplistic. What drives economies in most developed or developing countries is the desire to have a better standard of living. And that goes for all of us, spenders and savers alike. For some people it will mean spending money that they don't have at the moment – taking out a loan to get a new car, for example. For others, it will mean saving money to earn interest on it. And in order for the economy to function successfully, we need both types of person, but only as long as they lend and borrow responsibly.

97
I think that people often get into debt because they want a lifestyle that they can't really afford.

It's a lifestyle which is sold to them constantly through advertisements, for example, on TV and in magazines.

This desire to have a better lifestyle can affect some governments too. They want to improve their citizens' standard of living so that people will vote for them again.

99
/ʃ/: wash, machine, revolution
/tʃ/: watch, cheap, richer
/ʒ/: pleasure, decision, usually
/dʒ/: change, major, wages

100
I = Interviewer, R = Rick Castro
I: Most of us will be familiar with the concept of barter from our notions of how primitive societies work: you have a chicken I want and I've just made a new hunting spear that you need. So let's do a deal. But is 'barter' as a system of buying and selling goods and services coming back into fashion? With me is Rick Castro of the Barter Society. Rick, is this a serious alternative to current systems of trade or just a romantic notion?

R: The first thing I'd say is that barter never went out of fashion. People have been using barter as a way of exchanging goods for a lot longer than they have been using money and it is, as you've said, a feature of almost every primitive society past and present. But, it's also very much a feature of the modern economy. People are making bartering arrangements all the time – it's just that conventional economic statistics – GDP figures and so on – don't record it. How could they?

I: Can you give us an example of that?

R: Yes, I can, but firstly we should make an important distinction between direct barter – that's like the example you gave of two people exchanging a chicken for a spear – and then there's what we call 'exchange barter', which is where you belong to a barter group and make more indirect exchanges.

I: What does that mean?

R: Well, imagine I'm a yoga teacher and you're a tree surgeon. I need to have a tree cut down in my garden and I'm ready to offer you a whole year of yoga classes in return. But you don't want to do yoga. What happens then? Well, if we belong to a barter exchange group, like 'Bartercard'.

I: 'Bartercard'? You're not serious ...

R: Perfectly serious. If I belong to a group like that, I can sell my yoga classes for 'trade credits'. These can then be spent buying the goods or services of over 75,000 other members – restaurants, sports shops, almost anything. So if you're a member, I can buy your tree surgery services with my credits.

I: Hang on, though. This is just a tax dodge, isn't it? Normally I would have to pay tax on my tree surgery bill, wouldn't I? And you should charge tax on your yoga classes.

R: Of course these exchanges are liable to tax – at least that's the law in most developed countries.

I: So what's the advantage then? I'm trying hard to see one. Why not just use money?

R: Well, because if you belong to a group like that, it gives you access to a new market – a big circle of new contacts who will potentially become regular customers and possibly some of them your friends too!

🎵 101

A = Client, B = Caterer

A: So there'll be about sixty of us. We want some food but, to be honest, nothing too fancy. I suspect a lot of people will be going home and having supper later anyway.

B: OK, so what did you have in mind? A few canapés, some sandwiches?

A: Well, I was hoping we could have something a bit more exciting than sandwiches.

B: Perhaps if we prepared some sushi, some smoked salmon, a few samosas?

A: Yes, that would be much more like it. Is that going to be very pricey?

B: About £10 per person.

A: Mmm ... that's quite a lot, but let's face it, it is an important occasion. You know, it's a leaving party for someone who's been working with us for 37 years, so we don't want it looking cheap.

B: I think that's a good way to look at it. If I were in your shoes, I'd like to put on an event that people would remember. By the way, the £10 also includes the waiting staff for two hours.

A: Oh, we don't need that. We can just help ourselves. Would that reduce the price a bit, then?

B: No, I'm sorry. You have to appreciate that we have to come and set it all up and take it away anyway, so we might as well serve it while we're there.

A: I see. Well, the key thing for us is that it's a nice relaxing event, so we'll go with that, I guess.

B: Great. Just let me know exact numbers when you have them.

🎵 103

C = Caterer, MA = Model answer

1
C: So what kind of food did you have in mind? Some sandwiches?

MA: I was hoping we could have some hot food too.

2
C: OK. We could provide a few hot pastries as well. How does that sound?

MA: Yes, that would be great.

3
C: That would be about £10 per person.

MA: That's quite a lot. Could you move a bit on that price?

4
C: Sorry. You have to appreciate it's a lot of work for us. We could do it more cheaply but the food would be much more basic.

MA: No. The key thing for us is that it's nice food.

5
C: Well, if I were in your shoes, I would go for the more expensive menu.

MA: I suppose you're right. OK then. We'll do that.

IELTS Practice test

104

Presenter: In this test you'll hear a number of different recordings and you'll have to answer questions on what you hear. There will be time for you to read the instructions and questions and you will have a chance to check your answers. The recording will be played once only. The test is in four sections.

Now turn to Section 1 on page 100 of your book. You will hear a student called Martin telling his friend about a careers day which is being held in the city where they are studying. First you have some time to look at questions 1 to 5. You will see that there is also an example which has been done for you.

Now we shall begin. You should answer the questions as you listen, because you will not hear the recording a second time. Listen carefully and answer questions 1 to 5.

Woman: Hi, Martin. Did you hear about the careers day that the college is holding? My tutor was just talking about it.

Martin: Yeah, apparently there's something on the notice board about it, or so my flatmate was saying.

Woman: Well, it's probably this leaflet he saw pinned up there. Look, it's got all the details.

Martin: Great. Is it being held in the college then? I heard they were going to hire space in the Town Hall.

Woman: Really? I think you must be thinking of some other event. Our college is actually sharing the day with the technical university, and they're putting the day on at their campus. It's going to be outside in the grounds if the weather's nice.

Martin: Look, it goes on all day from ten till five. I wouldn't want to hang around that long though, just the morning or the afternoon would suit me fine. I start getting bored after a couple of hours at these things.

Woman: Well, look at the programme of talks – it'll help you decide which.

Martin: Anyway, there's a website with all the talks on, so it doesn't matter if you miss some of them.

Woman: Well, the event is free to students enrolled at the college, but the website isn't: you'd have to sign up like anybody else, and there's a monthly fee. But then you do see stuff from other similar events around the country too.

Martin: Sounds good. There are some sessions on in the lunchtime too. Look. And it's not the usual talks by old students or videos about voluntary work in other countries either. You can get tips on how to put a CV together or go to a seminar led by one of the big recruitment agencies.

Woman: Right. My careers advisor was recommending those when I met her for my one-to-one advice session the other day.

Martin: Should be good then.

Presenter: Before you listen to the rest of the conversation, you have some time to read questions 6 to 10.

Now listen and answer questions 6 to 10.

Martin: So what are the main talks on the programme, then?

Woman: Well, each faculty's put up one speaker. Our college in the morning and the technical university in the afternoon. But the speakers aren't only talking about stuff relevant to those subjects.

Martin: Sure. So let's see. It starts at ten and the Law faculty is putting up Professor Jaynes.

Woman: The famous judge?

Martin: No, you're thinking of James. This is Jaynes, J . A . Y . N . E . S. And he's talking about contracts of employment.

Woman: Oh right. Could be interesting though.

Martin: Maybe. But eleven o'clock you've got Professor Smith talking about internships – that should be more interesting. She lectures in accountancy, apparently. So which faculty's that? Economics?

Woman: Business Studies actually.

Martin: Oh yes, of course. Then Dr Wentworth is representing the Languages faculty at eleven. I heard her give a really good talk on cross-cultural misunderstandings last term – you know gestures and stuff you can get wrong – it was brilliant. But this time, she's doing technical translations.

Woman: Oh right. Yeah, she's a good speaker.

Martin: Then after lunch, there's Dr Shah from the Engineering faculty. It says here he's an expert in computer modelling, but he's going to be talking about openings in the construction industry.

Woman: Shame, I'd rather hear about the models.

Martin: Me too. Then there's Dr Bellucci from Sports Science – she's doing something on the Olympic Games which should be interesting – all the different jobs from different disciplines that are involved.

Woman: Right. And then it's our old friend Dr Fulton doing interview techniques. He's working in the Geology department at the technical university now, and they've put him up for this. Though when he was here, he was in the faculty of Geography.

Martin: Still he's a great speaker – always gets a laugh.

Woman: So what do you think …

Presenter: Now turn to Section 2 on page 102 of your book. You will hear some information about Jodrell Bank, a famous radio telescope, which is part of the University of Manchester. First you have some time to look at questions 11 to 14.

Now listen and answer questions 11 to 14.

Man: Good evening. I'm here to tell you about the Jodrell Bank Observatory, which has been a world leader in radio astronomy since the second half of the twentieth century. The site is part of the University of Manchester and there's also an arboretum with over 2,500 rare trees. A visitor centre provides information about both the famous radio telescope and the trees.

The giant Lovell Telescope that stands on the site is an internationally renowned and awe-inspiring landmark. This is a radio telescope so visitors cannot look through it directly. The observatory buildings are also still in use for operating the telescope, so are not usually open to the public. But the visitor centre provides a good view of the telescope and visitors can walk along a pathway not far from the base, where they will find plenty of notices providing information about the history of the telescope and how it works. The centre also provides opportunities to meet the scientists who work at the Observatory.

The visitor centre also provides activities for visitors of all ages. Admission prices at the centre vary according to the type of ticket and the season in which the visit is made. For example, an adult single ticket would cost £6.50 in the summer months and £5.50 at other times of year, whereas a family ticket would cost either £24 or £20. An annual ticket is available for individuals at £19.50 and for families at £60. Concessionary tickets are available at all times for children, students and retired people.

In terms of facilities available at the visitor centre, these are divided between two buildings: the Planet Pavilion, where you'll find the entrance as well as the glass-walled café with outside terrace – you get amazing views of the telescope from there. There's also a gift shop and a small exhibition space where visitors can learn about the planets. The second building is the Space Pavilion, which is the main exhibition area. Here visitors can find answers to the wonders of the universe, listen to the sound of the Big Bang and explore the universe using hands-on activities. As many returning visitors are aware, our planetarium was demolished in 2003, along with the old visitor centre. But we are looking to secure funding to restore this feature in the not-too-distant future.

Presenter: Before you hear the rest of the presentation, you have some time to look at questions 15 to 20.

Now listen and answer questions 15 to 20.

Man: Next, a bit about the history of the telescope. It's named after Sir Bernard Lovell, who was a pioneer in the study of astrophysics in the twentieth century. The site itself, which is about fifteen miles south of the other university buildings in Manchester, first came into the university's possession in 1939. It wasn't the Astrophysics department that bought it, though, but the Botany department who were looking for a place to cultivate wild plants. In 1945, Bernard Lovell was given some equipment to use in his work, including a radar. But because of electrical interference from trams passing the university buildings, it didn't work properly in central Manchester, so he asked to move it to Jodrell Bank instead. It was installed just in time to observe a meteor shower that was visible that year.

Over the next few years, Lovell installed other equipment on the site, including an aerial on a searchlight mount in 1946, and in 1947, the 218-foot Transit Telescope – at the time the largest in the world. This telescope was superseded by a larger and more up-to-date model in 1957. This was named the Mark One Telescope, later upgraded and eventually renamed the Lovell Telescope in honour of Sir Bernard. This telescope became famous in the 1960s for tracking manned and unmanned space missions, as well as providing information about astronomy itself. And the telescope remains a world leader in this field.

Further developments followed in the 1960s and 1970s, including a teaching telescope for use by undergraduates, and the creation of the arboretum in 1972. This features national collections of various rare trees and other plants as well as a scale model of the solar system.

More recent developments at the site have included the opening of a new Discovery Centre in 2011, an event which coincided with a decision to place Jodrell Bank on the UK shortlist for consideration as a site with World Heritage status. In July that year, the site also hosted a rock concert called 'Live from Jodrell Bank'. These are excellent examples of how the scientists at Jodrell Bank have always worked hard to engage with the wider community and increase the impact of their science.

Presenter: Now turn to Section 3 on page 103 of your book. You will hear an interview with a medical student called Damian, who is talking about his elective, a period of work experience he did overseas as part of his degree course. First you have some time to look at questions 21 to 24.

Now listen and answer questions 21 to 24.

Woman: Hi, Damian.

Damian: Hi.

Woman: Thanks for coming to talk to college radio about your elective. Now that's a period of work experience in a hospital you do in your final year as a medical student, isn't it?

Damian: That's right. The idea is that being a doctor is about understanding the psycho-social factors involved in each patient, as well as the medical ones. You do an elective in a speciality, to explore it in greater breadth and depth, and that's especially interesting when the placement's abroad.

Woman: So is it a sort of working holiday really?

Damian: No. I wouldn't say that. But electives do also give you the opportunity to travel and have fun. How you balance these two aspects is up to you. Whilst in Belize, I learned to scuba dive, climbed Mayan ruins and explored the jungle, not something you can say about every medical placement!

Woman: And it's up to you to organize the whole thing, isn't it?

Damian: That's right. Many students have problems when it comes to organizing an elective. For some it's the first time they've travelled alone or the first experience of being exposed to different cultures. I was cool with all that, but it's important to choose your speciality well. I had no idea where I wanted to go because I hadn't even chosen a speciality, so that made it tough.

Woman: Do you have to spend the whole period in one place, or can you split it up?

Damian: You can choose. I chose to divide mine into a six-week placement abroad and a two-week placement at home in the UK. Many people would argue that a two-week placement doesn't give you enough time to fit into a team and gain relevant experience, and I'd go along with that. With the benefit of hindsight, I'd have done better with a straight four-week split.

Woman: And where can you go for help with these decisions?

Damian: Well, many companies will organize elective placements for you, as well as providing cover and support ... at a price! But there are lots of companies out there, and I've heard that if you're willing to hunt around, you can find some reasonably priced deals. It's always worth asking round though. If you can talk to people about companies they've used, you can check whether those companies are any good or not. That's how I found the one I went with and I've no complaints.

Presenter: Before you hear the rest of the conversation, you have some time to look at questions 25 to 30.

Now listen and answer questions 25 to 30.

Woman: So Damian, tell us about your placement in Belize.

Damian: Well, having been undecided for a long time between specializing in surgery or emergency medicine, I went for emergency, because I thought it would give me a broader experience than surgery would. My first choice of country would've been Jamaica, but they only had places for dermatology and obstetrics, so that's how Belize came up. I'd never really heard of the country before.

Woman: And was it a company that helped you?

Damian: Yes, they provided photos of medical and non-medical facilities in a couple of different countries in the Caribbean and Central America. In the end, it wasn't the photos of the hospital, but those of the beach that drew me to Belize – perhaps I shouldn't admit to that!

Woman: So tell us a bit about working there.

Damian: The health system in Belize is a mixed one of both public and private. The government subsidizes a significant proportion of health care for the average Belizean, although there's a limited number of hospitals with in-patient facilities. Belize has an area of 22,000 square kilometres with only 300,000 people spread sparsely around it, and a big town is one with about 20,000 inhabitants. It means that a significant percentage of the population is rural based and nowhere near a free national hospital.

Woman: Right.

Damian: I was one of three British students placed by the company: the two others were in the south of the country and I think they had a different experience, but up in the north where I was, the biggest frustration was that despite Belize being an English-speaking country, the default language was Spanish, because a lot of the doctors working there are actually Cuban. I speak French, but not Spanish, so when consultations weren't in English, I needed the doctor to explain what had been said.

Woman: Would you go to Belize again?

Damian: Yes. And people do sometimes get jobs in the places they've been to on electives. But next time I wouldn't go with the idea of being a hospital doctor, I'd rather think of teaching the staff. But I think I could've made better use of my clinical experience if I'd learned basic Spanish – so that would be a priority before I went back.

Woman: Damian. Thanks.

Presenter: Now turn to Section 4 on page 104 of your book. You will hear a student giving a presentation about the Antiguan Racer Snake, a rare species living on a Caribbean island. First you have some time to look at questions 31 to 35.

Now listen and answer questions 31 to 35.

Woman: In my presentation today I want to talk about the rarest snake in the world – the Antiguan Racer Snake – an animal that has been rescued from the brink of extinction by the efforts of conservationists.

The snake is one of the racer snake family that is found in various regions across the Americas. It's a small harmless snake that grows to around one metre, with the female being slightly longer than the male.

Many of the racer snakes found in the Caribbean region, and especially those in the southern states of the USA, are black in colour, whereas the Antiguan Racer is lighter. The male is closer in colouring to the black racers, being a dark brown, whilst the female is distinguishable by its silver-grey skin.

The Antiguan Racer is found in various habitats, including sandy beaches and rocky ridges, but has a preference for dense undergrowth, which is one of the reasons why it's relatively rarely seen.

In terms of diet, the Antiguan Racer is very choosy. Other racer snakes feed on small mammals and amphibians such as frogs, but the Antiguan sub-species tends to rely on lizards as its main source of food. Maybe this is one of the reasons why it's an endangered species, although there's little evidence that its prey has ever been in short supply.

Presenter: Before you hear the rest of the presentation, you have some time to look at questions 36 to 40.

Now listen and answer questions 36 to 40.

Woman: By the end of the twentieth century, it was feared that the Antiguan Racer, which was once common on the large island of Antigua after which it's named, had indeed become extinct. And this was probably the case. The snake had once been common on the neighbouring island of Barbuda too, but hadn't survived the human development of these large islands. But the local inhabitants were convinced that the snakes might be surviving on one of the smaller islands off the Antiguan coast, such as Rabbit Island or Crump Island, or on Bird Island – the place where one was eventually spotted in 1995.

The tiny island was uninhabited and looked after by the Antiguan Forestry Unit, which was keen for scientists to establish how many snakes might be living there. They commissioned a six-week survey, to be carried out by one of the conservationists who had made the discovery, Mark Day, who later went on to work for the conservation body, Fauna and Flora International.

What was established by his work was that the small island, only measuring some 18,000 square metres, was supporting a racer population of around 100 individuals. The rarest snake in the world was alive and well, but seriously endangered. In 1996, a conservation project was set up to ensure its survival.

And with the current population standing at around 500 snakes, this project has been hailed a success. A captive breeding programme has been effective in increasing numbers, even though it was adversely affected by disease at first. Reintroduction to other nearby islands, and to the mainland of Antigua, has meant eradicating the rats that had decimated the snake population in the twentieth century – a programme that has worked, although the snake's habitat does remain vulnerable to hurricane damage. Now that the species is officially protected, there are unlikely to be further incursions of tourist development into its natural habitat, another cause of its earlier decline. The right kind of habitat is not found over a wide area, though, and this will eventually limit the extent of the snake population. So before I go on to ...

Answer key

Unit 1
1a (pages 4 and 5)

1
b

2
1 b   2 b   3 b   4 c   5 a   6 a

3
1 truth (line 6)   2 strength (line 9)   3 warmth (line 18)
4 length (line 25)   5 depth (line 36)

4
1 is dying out (line 1–2), France is changing and perhaps
  becoming (line 29–30)
2 we work with (line 3–4), we chat to (line 4), they reserve
  (real intimacy) (line 32)
3 friendships have lost (line 9), you have ever visited (line 17)
4 have been declining (line 12)

5
1 have you spent *or* have you been spending
2 Do you consider
3 do you have
4 is still increasing
5 Have you made
6 have you known
7 do you see
8 do you look for

6
1 intimate, close, strong   2 strong   3 close, true
4 complete   5 casual

7
1 student   2 companion   3 acquaintance   4 flat
5 blood   6 passing

8
1 serious, good fun
2 laid-back
3 unreliable
4 energetic
5 shy, outgoing
6 considerate

9
1 out with   2 up with   3 on   4 round   5 by   6 up with
7 up

1b (pages 6 and 7)

1
1 T   2 F   3 T   4 F   5 T   6 F

2
1 rate   2 boom   3 retirement   4 lifestyle
5 expectancy   6 developed

3
1 has declined, was
2 have improved, did
3 've also learned
4 has made, didn't have
5 have increased, was
6 has risen, 've been spending *or* are spending

4
1 have raised, hasn't been
2 has been encouraging, have reduced
3 have gone, was
4 had, has been going
5 has been looking, has had

5
1 last year   2 all morning   3 yet   4 before
5 since the age of sixteen   6 in the past   7 so far   8 just

6b
1 A: (Have) you finished using the computer yet? I need to
       check my emails.
   B: Yes, I **have**. But the internet connection (has) been a bit
       funny.
   A: What do you mean? **Have**n't you been able to connect
       or (has) it just been slow?
2 A: How (has) your visit to Scotland been? (Have) you had a
       good time?
   B: Well, the weather (has) been terrible, but apart from
       that, it's been wonderful.
   A: No, it **has**n't been a very nice summer, but I'm afraid
       that's pretty typical.

7
1 I think my parents' generation has been quite lucky.
2 My parents worked hard all their lives, but they both
  retired when they were sixty and they've been given good
  pensions. So now they can relax and enjoy themselves.
3 They've said that they don't want to be a burden on us,
  and that they don't expect us to look after them when
  they get old.
4 Considering that my husband and I will probably have to
  work until we are 68, I'm glad they said that.

1c (page 8)

1
c

2
1 F   2 T   3 T   4 T   5 F   6 T   7 F   8 F

3
1 a   2 a   3 c   4 b   5 b   6 c

4a
1 dyn<u>a</u>mic   2 fan<u>ta</u>stic   3 eco<u>no</u>mics   4 gener<u>a</u>tion
5 re<u>stric</u>tion   6 tra<u>di</u>tion
Rule: The penultimate syllable is always stressed.

4b
spe<u>ci</u>fic   <u>i</u>talics   te<u>rri</u>fic   scien<u>ti</u>fic   characte<u>ri</u>stic
im<u>pre</u>ssion   re<u>la</u>tion   inte<u>rru</u>ption   transfor<u>ma</u>tion
compre<u>hen</u>sion

1d (page 9)

1
1 –   2 for   3 –   4 –   5 about   6 –   7 on   8 from   9 in
10 with

2a
1 PPS   2 PPC   3 PPS   4 PPC

2b
1 present perfect continuous
2 present perfect simple

3
1 been wondering   2 been working   3 decided
4 been helping   5 finished   6 lost

4
a Fancy bumping into you here
b What a nice surprise
c it obviously suits you
d how's it all going with you
e Do give her my best regards
f great to see you
g Good luck with the job

5a
1 are things
2 I'm doing fine
3 're looking very well
4 's been ages
5 should probably get back
6 I've got to rush

6
Students' own answers.

1e (page 10)

1
1 g   2 c   3 f   4 e   5 a   6 d   7 b

2
1 you're able to **get by** (manage)
2 I **got** a letter (received)
3 I'm trying not to **get** too excited (become)
4 to **get** a job (obtain)
5 Eva is going to **get** married (be)
6 when you **get** a moment to write (have)

3
1 understand   2 put down *or* stop speaking on
3 bought   4 arrive at *or* reach   5 take *or* catch
6 recover from   7 won   8 find *or* bring *or* fetch

4
1 received *or* got   2 am   3 arrived *or* got   4 sounds
5 have had *or* have been having   6 were *or* got
7 hope   8 have recovered
9 hasn't become *or* hasn't got / doesn't become *or* doesn't get
10 sounds   11 don't think   12 have ever experienced
13 has happened   14 am trying *or* have tried *or* have been
trying   15 haven't been   16 find *or* get   17 helped *or* has
helped *or* has been helping   18 don't really understand *or*
don't really get

Wordbuilding / Learning skills / Check! (page 11)

1
-ful: respectful, helpful, successful (also 'careful')
-ish: foolish, childish, selfish
-ive: sensitive, decisive, supportive
-ious/-ous: ambitious, adventurous, humorous
-ent/-ant: dependent, confident, patient
-al: practical, emotional, traditional
-ing: caring, controlling, loving
-ate: considerate, fortunate, passionate

2
Possible answers:
1 dependent   2 caring   3 traditional   4 patient
5 controlling   6 practical   7 humorous   8 fortunate
9 successful   10 ambitious

3
1 decisively   2 take   3 indecisive   4 conclusion

4
Students' own answers.

5
1 b   2 a   3 a and c   4 c   5 b

Unit 2

2a (pages 12 and 13)

1
b

2
1 b   2 c   3 c   4 c   5 a

3
1 a   2 b   3 b   4 c   5 b

4
1 drove   2 made   3 arrived   4 was getting   5 climbed
6 had gone   7 were hanging   8 put   9 moved   10 trapped
11 stood *or* was standing   12 had crushed *or* was
crushing   13 hadn't told   14 had already been waiting
15 had decided

5
1 b   2 a   3 c

6
1 had been cycling   2 had left   3 started
4 was shining   5 checked   6 cut

7
1 crashed   2 top   3 stuck   4 cat   5 sung   6 drunk

8
1 drama   2 background   3 main   4 key   5 setting
6 theme   7 moving   8 touching   9 funny   10 filmed

9a
The tenses used to describe the film are: present simple,
present continuous and present perfect.

9b
1 gives   2 begin   3 reaches *or* has reached
4 grow *or* are growing   5 are getting

2b (pages 14 and 15)

1
1 That they walk hundreds of miles (across Antarctica) to
   reach their breeding ground.
2 The struggle between life and death.

2
1 have chicks   2 their young   3 dramatic
4 predictable   5 in such hard conditions

3
1 are left, is described
2 was made, was (also) inspired, was impressed
3 haven't (really) been approached
4 will not be fed
5 can be (easily) predicted

4
1
was also **inspired** <u>by</u> the incredible beauty of Antarctica,
the action **is described** <u>by</u> a narrator
They **haven't** really **been approached** <u>by</u> humans before
I **was** really **impressed** <u>by</u> that
2
are left (by the females)
will not be fed (by their mothers)
where the film was made (by the director)
can be easily predicted (by us / by the filmmakers)

5
1 The original French version of *March of the Penguins* was
   released in 2005.
2 In 2006 it was given the award for best documentary by
   the Academy of Motion Arts and Sciences.
3 The film can be seen in over twenty different languages.
4 In the English version, the penguins' voices had been
   changed to the voice of a narrator.
5 The film has been praised for its interest and beauty by
   critics all over the world.
6 Comparisons between the lives of penguins and humans
   have also been made.

6
1 I am often asked that question
2 All of them have been challenged by difficult situations.
3 You are not bothered by the cold so much. *or* You are not bothered so much by the cold.
4 So (your) movement must be kept to a minimum.

7a
1 were   2 been   3 will   4 are   5 is   6 was, been

8
1 engage, tell   2 present   3 expressed *or* summed up
4 share   5 brought   6 express *or* sum up

9
1 setting for; thought-provoking book
2 characters are you and me and every other typical passenger
3 book is based on conversations that the author had
4 The idea behind it; can portray modern civilization

2c (page 16)

1
1 T   2 T   3 T   4 F   5 F

2
1 children; adults   2 fairy tale   3 sadness   4 moved
5 moral lessons

3
1 a fine-looking   2 watches closely   3 stops to rest on
4 asks   5 people   6 days   7 becomes ill   8 destroy

4
1 a   2 b

5
1 kept their promise
2 kept an eye on
3 keep him company
4 keep track of
5 keep a record
6 keep a secret

2d (page 17)

1
1 tore   2 broke   3 stuck   4 made   5 froze   6 burst

2
a What a
b That was
c How *or* That was
d How *or* That was
e What
f How
g Poor
h What a *or* That must have been
i How *or* That must have been
j What a *or* That must have been a

Possible answers:
1 a *or* c   2 a *or* j   3 a *or* c *or* i   4 c   5 a   6 a *or* j

3
1 Hannah's passport was out of date.
2 She went to the passport office in London to get a new passport.
3 Very stressed.

4
1 Poor   2 awful   3 luck   4 stressful   5 sympathize   6 same

6
Students' own answers.

2e (page 18)

1a
whispered, replied anxiously, moaned, muttered, cried

1b
1 c   2 b   3 g   4 d   5 e   6 a   7 f

2a
1 He said, ⊘What a surprise!⊘
2 ⊘I know,⊘ she said, that you don't like eating spicy food.⊘
3 ⊘Do you agree?⊘he asked.
4 ⊘I don't agree,⊘he said.

2b
'I don't think this is going to work,' Christopher sighed. 'We've been trying to build this canoe for three days and it still looks like a lump of wood. The wood's too hard,' he added. 'Actually, Christopher,' said Jen encouragingly, 'we are making some progress. What we really need to do is find some better tools.' Just then Tom screamed, 'I've got it! Instead of using our penknives directly on the wood, why don't we make some better tools using our knives?'

3
Model answer:
'Look out,' screamed Fergus, 'I think he's angry now.' The two friends edged nervously backwards as the snake turned its head to face them. Josh had thrown a large rock at it, hoping that this would frighten it, but it seemed that it had had the opposite effect. Now Josh was looking around for something else to hit the snake with. 'Where's a stick when you need one?' he muttered. 'Too late for that,' said Fergus. 'Let's get out of here.' And with that, he leaped towards the trees and started running.

Wordbuilding / Learning skills / Check! (page 19)

1
1 made   2 take   3 shared   4 paying   5 catch   6 take
7 get   8 telling   9 expresses   10 catch   11 committed
12 do   13 give   14 makes

2
1 b   2 a   3 a   4 b   5 b   6 a

3, 4 and 5
Students' own answers.

6
1
a a documentary
b a children's story *or* fairy tale
c a fantasy film

2
a film director *or* producer
b author *or* writer
c racing driver

3
a keep
b nightmare
c flames

Unit 3

3a (pages 20 and 21)

1
c

2
1 rich   2 increase   3 more   4 look after them   5 8.3
6 there are three ways

3
1 rises   2 boost   3 grown   4 increase   5 peak
6 decrease *or* decreasing   7 fall   8 go down
9 lessening   10 reduce

4
1 reduce   2 grow *or* increase *or* rise   3 fall *or* go down
4 reduce *or* lessen   5 increase *or* boost   6 increase

5
1 will have, will be
2 will rely
3 I'll tell, I'll be, doesn't start
4 won't solve
5 is going to
6 I'm going, begins

6
1 Are you going *or* Are you going to go
2 are you getting *or* are you going to get
3 'll probably drive *or* 'm probably going to drive
4 'll go
5 'll give
6 are you leaving *or* are you going to leave
7 starts
8 'll finish *or* 'll be finished

7
1 etcetera   2 contributed   3 lot   4 fifteen   5 years
6 powerful   7 motives   8 meet   9 secretly
10 years

3b Smart technology (pages 22 and 23)

1
Items mentioned: kitchen gadgets, water use,
sound-proofing, visual media, lighting

2
1 a   2 b   3 c   4 c   5 c   6 b

3
1 b   2 f   3 a   4 c   5 e   6 d

4
1 will be hearing   2 will be making   3 will all be
using   4 will have become   5 will be using
6 will be cleaning   7 will be installing   8 will have
become   9 will be launching

5
1 will be doing   2 will be cleaning   3 will have developed
4 will be doing   5 will have been   6 won't have acquired

6
1 cardboard   2 brick   3 Cotton   4 leather   5 concrete
6 rubber

7
1 d   2 e   3 c   4 f   5 a   6 b   7 g   8 h

8
1 information age, information overload, information
  technology
2 data security, data storage
3 computer games, computer graphics, computer
  programmer

9
1 data security   2 information age   3 computer
  graphics   4 data storage   5 information overload

10
1 The weekday edition of *The New York Times* contains more
  information than the average person in 17th-century
  England learned in a lifetime.
2 Around a thousand books are published internationally
  every day and the total of all printed knowledge doubles
  every five years.
3 More information has been published in the last thirty
  years than in the previous 5,000.

3c (page 24)

1
1 b   2 c   3 c   4 b

2
1 2007; 6,000   2 99.9%   3 6   4 700   5 30   6 2010

3
1 works   2 provides   3 contains   4 lasts   5 weighs   6 run

4a
1 /ɪ/   2 /ɪ/   3 /aɪ/   4 /ɪ/   5 /aɪ/

5
1 neat   2 appropriate   3 consuming   4 handy   5 cutting   6 fix

3d (page 25)

1
1 blocked   2 loose   3 stuck   4 broken   5 cracked
6 squeaking   7 blank   8 faulty

2
Possible answers:
1 blank, cracked, faulty
2 loose, squeaking, stuck
3 broken, faulty
4 blocked, cracked
5 broken, faulty, loose, squeaking

3
1 ceiling fan
2 it doesn't look very safe or may have become loose
3 use the desk fan
4 TV
5 the screen is blank
6 switch the monitor on separately *or* use the on/off button
  on the screen (rather than the remote control)

4
1 wonder, look
2 seems to be
3 working, may
4 supposed, won't
5 get, whatever
6 tried
7 try

5
The two verbs which do not fit the stress pattern are:
highlight and *open*

3e (page 26)

1
1 Please can/could I pick up my bicycle on my way home from
  work tonight? *or* Can/Could I please pick up my bicycle on
  my way home from work tonight? *or* Can/Could I pick up
  my bicycle on my way home from work tonight, please?
2 I wonder if you can/could help me.
3 Do you have any idea where I can find a battery charger
  for my old phone?
4 Could you send me an instruction manual for my washing
  machine, please? *or* Could you please / Please could you
  send me an instruction manual for my washing machine?
5 Please can/could you advise me how to … *or* Could you
  please advise me how to …?
6 Do you know what the phone number for Apricot
  Computers is?
7 Would you mind showing me how to use Powerpoint?
8 Could/Can you please tell me what number I should call
  to get technical advice?

2
a interest   b practice   c business   d print   e date
f order   g way   h luck

3
1 g 2 a 3 e 4 d 5 h 6 c 7 b 8 f

4
Model answer:

Hi Jim

I hope all is well with you. I tried to call you earlier, but I couldn't get any answer. I wonder if you could help me. I've just bought a new hi-fi system, but I can't set it up. The speakers aren't working, but I don't understand the instructions. Would you mind calling me some time? I'll be at home this evening.

Many thanks

Sam

Wordbuilding / Learning skills / Check! (page 27)

1
address book
battery life
credit card
data protection
information technology
news story
instruction manual
travel agent

2
1 estate, travel
2 office, kitchen
3 bottle, can
4 video, board
5 coffee, lunch
6 ironing, message

3
1 travel agent, credit card
2 information technology, instruction manual
3 news story, video game
4 credit card, coffee break *or* lunch break

4
Students' own answers.

5
1 gadget 2 lazy 3 overpopulation 4 by
5 Appropriate 6 luck
Word: global

Unit 4

4a (pages 28 and 29)

1
1 In the first photo, the graffiti has been drawn on public walls. In the second photo, the graffiti is part of a piece of artwork.
2 Students' own answers.

2
1 being put in jail
2 shouldn't
3 the property owner

3
1 c 2 b 3 c 4 c 5 a 6 a

4
1 every member of the club
2 either method works *or* either method would work
3 any celebrities at the opening night
4 all our money
5 countries have their own laws and rules
6 whole world is waiting to see what will happen

5
1 each, all 2 no 3 both 4 any 5 Every 6 no
7 whole 8 Either

6
1 no 2 all the 3 the whole 4 each 5 Both

7
1 artwork 2 exhibition 3 artist 4 gallery 5 street
6 artistic 7 fine 8 arty

8
1 The message was clear: is this how far we have come since the Stone Age?
2 Often it carries a political or social message, but in an amusing way that ordinary people can relate to.
3 Despite not calling himself an artist, his work has been shown in galleries and has sold for thousands of dollars.
4 Banksy, who is based in the UK, is perhaps the world's best-known graffiti artist.
5 Banksy loves to surprise. In 2005, a picture showing a primitive human being pushing a shopping cart appeared in the British Museum.

The correct order is: 4, 3, 2, 5, 1

4b (pages 30 and 31)

1
1 show, performer 2 gig, venue, band 3 exhibition, gallery 4 buskers, halls 5 play, musical

2
1 Batman Live, This is Design
2 The Alternative Village Fete, Notting Hill Carnival
3 The Alternative Village Fete, Notting Hill Carnival
4 The Alternative Village Fete
5 The Floating Cinema
6 Notting Hill Carnival
7 Batman Live
8 The Alternative Village Fete

3
1 communal 2 float 3 eye candy 4 mundane
5 take for granted 6 workshop

4
1 a little 2 enough 3 a lot of, A large number of
4 plenty of, no 5 a lack of 6 many 7 hardly any
8 a bit of

5
1 number 2 no 3 several *or* some 4 plenty *or* loads *or* lots
5 any 6 few

4c (page 32)

1
1 country music 2 dance music 3 (punk) rock (music)
4 hip-hop (music)

2
Suggested answers:
a 3 b 1 c 1 d 4 e 2 f 2

3
1 Country; real
2 influences
3 teenagers; rock
4 sounds; technology

4
1 be connected to 2 escape 3 seem true 4 discover
5 think of 6 (not) be important

5
1 He spends a fortune on clothes every month.
2 I spent two hours trying to find their house.

3 She spends money like there's no tomorrow.
4 We haven't spent much time together recently.
5 They spent £20,000 on renovating their house.
6 See how you manage, but don't spend ages on it.
7 Why don't you spend the night with us on Tuesday?
8 She has spent her whole life trying to help people.

4d (page 33)

1
1 the Amazon River (and the people who live and work around the river)   2 He likes the presenter.

2
1 X   2 X   3 X

3
1 kind of thing   2 feel particularly inspired   3 a big fan of
4 got on my nerves   5 listen to him   6 a bit tired of

4
1 I could listen to Bach all day.
2 Documentaries don't really do anything for me.
3 I'm not really into TV.
4 I'm not particularly keen on the presenter.
5 I get a bit tired of reality TV shows.
6 I don't generally watch much TV *or* I don't generally watch TV much.

5
1 documentary   2 everywhere   3 specifically   4 interest
5 separate   6 restaurant   7 listener   8 general

6
Students' own answers.

4e (page 34)

1
a I, we and you; it   b active; passive   c contracted; uncontracted   d formal   e Avoid   f furthermore
g Share

2
Possible answers:
¹ I've got to admit that ² I'm ³ not a big fan of stand-up comedy. ⁴ I always think that it's a rather unnatural thing. The comedian ⁵ stands up in front of an audience who stare at him or her as if to say, 'Come on, then, make me laugh.' The comedian then has a few minutes to make them laugh or the audience will start to get restless. It's all a bit too aggressive for me. ⁶ So when ⁷ I went with an old school friend to see new British comedian Spencer Brown last Tuesday night at the Bristol Comedy Club, ⁸ I wasn't really looking forward to it.

1 contraction
2 contraction
3 personal details
4 share your feelings
5 active verb
6 conversational linking phrase
7 active verb
8 share your feelings

3
Possible answers:
1 But   2 weren't   3 the rest of the audience seemed to like his act   4 start   5 you think at first   6 then *or* after that
7 that's   8 putting together   9 in fact *or* actually

4
Model answer:
The secret of the show's success is that Spencer Brown really understands his audience and what people find funny. Not only that, but he comes across as a nice guy too. If you are in Bristol, I'd definitely recommend going

to see him. He'll be at the Bristol Comedy Club until Saturday 10th December. You'll be smiling for weeks afterwards!

Wordbuilding / Learning skills / Check! (page 35)

1
1 bookshop   2 book club   3 booking   4 fully booked
5 bookish   6 booking office   7 bookkeeper   8 bookmark
9 do things by the book   10 booklet

2
1 fully booked   2 bookkeeper   3 bookmarks   4 booklet
5 booking   6 bookish

4
1 No, not really.
2 /ˈkʌmftəbl/
3 You use *either* + singular noun, but *both* + plural noun.
4 Yes, 'it gets on my nerves'.
5 American
6 Yes, it's quite direct.

5
1a full   b Melbourne   c such
2a a few   b folk   c fine (art)
3a an impersonal tone   b a lot of luck   c spend a fortune
4a gig, busker   b gallery, arty   c play, musical

Unit 5

5a (pages 36 and 37)

1
1 F   2 T   3 T   4 F

2
1 back to normal 2 floods *or* flood waters, winds   3 resettle
4 co-ordinated   5 depressed   6 safe   7 imaginative *or* innovative   8 practical

3
1 to be   2 seeing   3 to hold   4 to return   5 to resettle
6 building   7 seeing   8 wondering

4
verb + *to* + infinitive: ask, help, hope, want
verb + *someone* + *to* + infinitive: allow, ask, get, help, want
verb + *-ing*: carry on, enjoy, imagine
verb + *someone* + infinitive: help, make

5a
verb + *to* + infinitive: choose, learn
verb + *someone* + *to* + infinitive: force, teach
verb + *-ing*: avoid, finish, involve, (not) mind
verb + *someone* + infinitive: let

5b
1 to visit   2 rebuild *or* to rebuild   3 to participate   4 doing
5 to work   6 learning   7 to do   8 meeting

6
1 pedestrian   2 centre   3 residential   4 luxury   5 spaces
6 blocks   7 park   8 centre

7
1 knock down   2 turn into   3 spoil   4 modernize
5 redevelop

8a
The fact that most people have returned says a lot about how special this city is. The people who live here can't imagine living anywhere else.
I'm a musician and making a living in New Orleans has always been a challenge. We hoped to see more investment in jobs and tourism after the hurricane.
But since Hurricane Katrina, life has definitely become

harder. I love this city, but these days, I'm forced to go out of town to find work.

Answer: Yes, the resident is happy living in New Orleans.

8b

1 can't imagine living   2 hoped to see   3 'm forced to go

5b (pages 38 and 39)

1

Sentences a and b are true of Monterey today.

2

1 T   2 N   3 F   4 T   5 T   6 T   7 F   8 T

3

1 dynamic   2 join (in) the party
3 just like that   4 old-timers   5 set up   6 sample

4

1 dynamic   2 industrial   3 attractive   4 preserved
5 regulated   6 essential

5

1 NC   2 NC   3 C   4 C   5 NC   6 NC   7 C   8 C

6

1 going   2 putting   3 catching   4 to say *or* saying
5 fishing   6 to make   7 to go   8 eating

7

1 to visit   2 to see   3 to open   4 to do   5 having

8

China – minor	placed – taste
found – drowned	rule – tool
front – hunt	way – weigh
meant – sent	whale – they'll
ocean – motion	where – share

5c (page 40)

1

1 in later life   2 things   3 talk   4 technology   5 three

2

1 language ability, overall development and success (in life)
2 in, off
3 seeing the child as a true conversation partner or having a
  conversation with your baby/child
4 that babies respond to what you are saying a long time
  before they can speak
5 digital media
6 thirty million

3

1 key   2 spatial awareness   3 commentary
4 facial expression   5 interacting   6 statistic

4

1 behind   2 for   3 through   4 apart   5 out   6 over *or* off

5b

<u>c</u>ommentary   <u>d</u>ominate   em<u>p</u>athy   in<u>f</u>luence   <u>p</u>owerful
a<u>b</u>ility   de<u>v</u>elopment   tech<u>no</u>logy

5d (page 41)

1

1 d   2 e   3 g   4 a   5 c   6 f   7 b

2

1 public   2 local   3 green   4 pedestrianized
5 leisure

3

Conversation 1: b
Conversation 2: e

4

1 I find it
2 I agree completely
3 The thing is
4 absolutely
5 For me,
6 make much more sense
7 understand
8 you also need to consider
9 I'm more concerned
10 Not necessarily.

5

1 I <u>know</u> and I agree <u>completely</u>.
2 The thing <u>is</u>, it's our <u>taxes</u> they're <u>spending</u>.
3 For <u>me</u>, that would make <u>much</u> more <u>sense</u>.
4 I <u>understand</u> why you <u>say</u> that.
5 But <u>actually</u>, you <u>also</u> need to <u>consider</u> all the <u>old</u> people.

6

Students' own answers.

5e (page 42)

1

1 B   2 D   3 A   4 C

2

c quoting what someone (often famous) has said about this problem

3

Possible answers:
(giving a dramatic example) You used to be able to drive from Washington to Boston, a distance of 450 miles, through rich, green landscape. Now the only green you see is the paint on people's houses!

(giving some statistics) In the United States, the area between Boston and Washington DC, a distance of 450 miles, is now a massive urban region with a population of about fifty million – that's almost 17% of the US population on 2% of the US land area.

4

1 In addition
2 Because of this; As a result
3 on the other hand

5b

1 … three acres of land, the house comes with a swimming
   pool. *or* … coming with three acres of land, the house has
   a swimming pool.
2 … rising crime, people have moved out of the centre. *or* …
   a rise in crime, …
3 … a good bus service, we have excellent roads into the
   city centre. *or* … having a good bus service, we have
   excellent roads into the city centre.
4 … restrictions on building on green spaces, we are starting
   to redevelop city centres.

Wordbuilding / Learning skills / Check! (page 43)

1

1 badly, well
2 short-term, long-term
3 newly, well
4 highly, well
5 quietly, highly
6 poorly, cleverly
7 culturally, socially
8 reasonably, extremely

2

1 long-term unemployed
2 reasonably well-off

3 quietly confident
4 cleverly designed
5 badly prepared
6 culturally mixed
7 highly educated
8 newly built

4
Possible answers:
- It doesn't say who wrote it, but it doesn't seem to be a travel article. The interest seems to be from an urban development perspective.
- The main argument is that a fantastic city has grown up in a place you would not expect it, because of one person's dream and ambition.
- The writer doesn't say whether he/she likes what has happened to Dubai or not, but he/she seems uncertain that it will be a long-term success.
- I agree with the writer's argument. It seems an unsustainable development.

5
1 c   2 c   3 c   4 a and c   5 b

Unit 6

6a (pages 44 and 45)

1
Speaker 1: c
Speaker 2: e
Speaker 3: f
Speaker 4: b
The two extra items are a and d.

2
Speaker 1: d   Speaker 2: f   Speaker 3: b   Speaker 4: a
The two extra activities are c and e.

3
1 a   2 b   3 b   4 b   5 c

4
1 Let's not pretend	6 I hope not
2 Don't answer	7 not to let the children
3 You don't have to do	know
4 not to go	8 you really mustn't let
5 I don't think it's	
extravagant	

5
1 I'm afraid not, sorry.
2 I don't think it's a great idea.
3 Let's not do anything to upset them.
4 I hope I didn't give her the wrong impression.
5 You don't have to give the book back to me immediately.
6 Try not to be late, please.
7 You mustn't take food into the library.
8 None of them (there) knew the answer, not even the teacher.

6
1 off or holiday   2 catering   3 scenery   4 view
5 airlines   6 luggage or baggage   7 journey or drive or way
8 countryside   9 took   10 suitcase or bag

7
1 sunbathing   2 guided   3 souvenirs   4 snorkelling
5 sightseeing   6 riding   7 eating out   8 beachcombing

8
1 In tough economic times, people will try not to spend so much on luxuries and that includes holidays.
2 However, they don't want to go without a holiday altogether, because holidays are an important break from the stresses of work and daily life.
3 You don't have to go abroad to go on holiday. You can have a staycation instead. These have increased in popularity in recent years.
4 I don't think it's a bad trend because it means that people discover more about their own country, and at the same time, they boost the local economy.

6b (pages 46 and 47)

1
1 print off boarding pass
2 buy guidebook and suntan lotion
3 check travel insurance is up to date
4 write down contact details or write contact details down
5 get vaccinations before travelling
6 check passport is valid

2
1 consultancy-type roles   2 highly skilled professionals
3 four to six months   4 no costs

3
1 c   2 b   3 a   4 c   5 c   6 b

4
1 rewarding   2 tough   3 lasting   4 fresh   5 suited to
6 flexible

5
1 do you   2 wouldn't it   3 is it   4 didn't you
5 mightn't there   6 wouldn't I

6
1 me what kind of expenses you cover
2 it would harm my future career to take time away from work to volunteer
3 Wouldn't you like to use your skills to help others
4 if there are organizations which offer long-term volunteering jobs for inexperienced people
5 It's a bit selfish to volunteer just because you want to travel, isn't it
6 Surely it's more interesting to see another country as a volunteer rather than as a tourist

7
1 F   2 F   3 R   4 R   5 R   6 F   7 R   8 F

6c (page 48)

1
Items on *NG Endeavour*: cruises: a swimming pool, a library, professional photographers, kayaking trips, wildlife excursions, expert guides

2
1 fishing   2 sun   3 fitness   4 lounge   5 Islands   6 kayaks
7 naturalist   8 $1,000   9 day   10 Ecuadorian

3
1 comfortable   2 educational   3 adventurous   4 expensive

4
1 sleek   2 cranes   3 base   4 unique   5 remote

5
1 **If you had a cruise in mind**, try one of Lindblad's expeditions.
2 **If you don't mind a bit of danger and excitement**, Lindblad cruises are perfect.
3 I meant to book this holiday, but **I've had a lot on my mind** (lately).
4 **Bear in mind that** these are not typical cruises.
5 I used to think that cruises were for the retired, but **I've changed my mind** now.
6 **I'm in two minds about going** on one of their cruises.

6b
1 Don't   2 No   3 It doesn't   4 No   5 Don't   6 It doesn't

6d (page 49)

1
1 in   2 up   3 to   4 on   5 out   6 on   7 up   8 out *or* down

2
1 He's working. *or* He's at work.
2 He'll get a bus, then walk.
3 At Steve's office.

3
1 The easiest thing is to take the bus.
2 Alternatively, I can (just) take a taxi.
3 I can make my own way.
4 It's only a fifteen-minute bus ride.
5 I'm coming in by train.
6 If I get held up, I'll let you know.

4
1 drive   2 flight   3 ride   4 walk   5 ride   6 crossing

5a
1 d   2 b   3 a   4 e   5 c

6
Students' own answers.

6e (page 50)

1
1 She had to pay £30/extra charges to carry her coat onto the plane.
2 She wants a refund and she wants the airline to investigate the matter.

2
1 Oxford   2 customer – company   3 formal

3
1 register a complaint   2 unjust   3 stated   4 informed
5 placed   6 attempted   7 wished   8 opted
9 these circumstances   10 investigate

3b
Model answer:

Dear Sir/Madam

I am writing to **register a complaint** about the meal we **were served** on our flight home last week – flight UZ332. On the booking confirmation it **stated** that we **would be given** breakfast and lunch. **However**, breakfast **only consisted of** a cup of tea and lunch a tuna sandwich. By itself, this would not have been a problem, but **I regret to say that** my husband and I both **suffered** food poisoning from the sandwich.

4
Model answer:

Given the circumstances, I would ask you to do two things. Firstly, please ensure that in future communication with passengers you make it clear what kind of meal will be served. Secondly, please ensure that the food which you provide is fresh and has not been stored in the wrong conditions.

Yours faithfully

Thomas Garcia

Wordbuilding / Learning skills / Check! (page 51)

1
1 in   2 out   3 out   4 in   5 out   6 in   7 in   8 out
9 up   10 in

2
a fall out (with)   b take in   c drop in (on)   d look in (on)
e fall in (with)   f look out   g give in (to)   h take out
i drop out (of)   j give up

3
1 reason for writing   2 link the ideas   3 examples
4 spelling

4
1 Because it's a letter of complaint to a person you don't know.
2 Reason for writing; details or facts about the incident; action wanted
3 At the time (that); consequently; Otherwise; Given these circumstances
4 formal
5 She didn't want to delay other passengers; it's not unreasonable to wear a coat onto a plane

5
1 She took a Japanese holiday in her own city (New York).
2 voluntourism
3 in a prison hotel
4 in an art hotel, e.g. Propeller Island City Lodge, in Berlin
5 couch surfing

Unit 7

7a (pages 52 and 53)

1
Speaker 1: e
Speaker 2: d
Speaker 3: a
Speaker 4: c

2
a 2   b 4   c 2   d 1   e 3   f 4

3
1 b   2 a   3 a   4 c   5 b   6 a

4
1 are, provide
2 don't, are
3 don't, decide, will make
4 try, will end
5 are, have

5
1 'll feel, manage
2 promise
3 'm going to reserve *or* 'll reserve, is
4 will get, returns *or* has returned
5 'll just read, 'm waiting *or* wait
6 hear *or* 've heard, 'll let
7 wins, 'll take
8 find *or* 've found
9 'll cook, get
10 won't have *or* doesn't want to have, 's living

6
1 brought   2 spoil   3 punished   4 tell   5 disobey
6 nagging   7 rebelled   8 give   9 reward

7
Everything depends on what you see as the future role of your children. In other words, what is it that you are raising them to do?
Do you want them to be good members of society?
If so, you will teach them values such as obeying the law, co-operating with others and generally being good citizens.
Or do you want them to be successful individuals?
If so, you will help them to be free thinkers and to be independent.
Or is it important that they are good family members? Then you will teach them to respect their elders and to follow family traditions.

7b (pages 54 and 55)

1
b

2
1 b   2 c   3 a   4 a   5 c

3
1 used to eat   2 weren't used to seeing   3 would use
4 would have   5 are used to eating   6 have got used to
eating   7 usually eat out   8 are used to seeing   9 used to
eat   10 usually eat

4
1 didn't use to cook   2 used to cook   3 wanted
4 used to hang *or* would hang   5 was   6 had
7 used to cook *or* would cook   8 were used to doing *or*
used to do

5a
/uː/: blue, lunar, rude, suit, truce
/juː/: consume, fortune, humanity, humour, menu,
used, usually

6
1 P, SF
2 D, F
3 F, P *or* S, SD
4 P, SD *or* D

7c (page 56)

1
1 F   2 F   3 T   4 F   5 F   6 T

2
1 d   2 b

3
1 rather   2 Unlike   3 little   4 such   5 At worst

5
1 all the same   5 a difference of opinion
2 the same coin   6 no difference
3 a different matter   7 a different tune
4 the same thing   8 the same boat

7d (page 57)

1
1 honeymoon   2 reception   3 stag   4 veil   5 engagement
6 groom *or* bridegroom   7 fiancé(e)

2
1 It's a sign of wealth and social status.
2 Because the bride didn't go out to work (so this was her
  financial contribution to the marriage).
3 the bride's family
4 the groom's family
5 They bring gifts.
6 clothes and jewellery

3
1 symbolizes   2 rule   3 customary   4 marks   5 occasion
6 place   7 traditional   8 On

4
1 /z/   2 /s/   3 /z/   4 /s/   5 /s/   6 /z/   7 /s/   8 /s/
9 /z/   10 /s/   11 /z/   12 /z/

5
Students' own answers.

7e (page 58)

1
1 e   2 c   3 a   4 d   5 b

2
1 romantic
2 magnificent
3 bright red
4 spectacular, colourful, magical

3
1 takes place   2 marks   3 begin   4 highlight   5 gathers
6 dancing

Wordbuilding / Learning skills / Check! (page 59)

1
1 bits and pieces   7 life and soul
2 bride and groom   8 plans and arrangements
3 husband and wife   9 pomp and ceremony
4 food and drink   10 singing and dancing
5 friends and family   11 suit and tie
6 fun and games   12 time and trouble

2
1 pomp and ceremony   2 time and trouble   3 bits and
pieces   4 life and soul   5 friends and family   6 suit and tie

5
1 in   2 out   3 at   4 of   5 up   6 to   7 with   8 off

Unit 8

8a (pages 60 and 61)

1
1 target   2 come   3 live   4 aim   5 have   6 achieved

2

Speaker	Their ambition	What they were doing before
1 Rhea	to help children get a good education	working for a big insurance company
2 Sasha	to work in the art world	(went to art college) painting as a hobby working as a waiter / working in bars

3
1 a   2 c   3 b   4 b   5 c   6 c

4
1 b   2 b   3 a   4 a   5 b   6 b

5
1 had felt, would have carried
2 hadn't told, wouldn't be
3 were still learning, would probably be
4 was, wouldn't have moved
5 hadn't found, wouldn't have been
6 hadn't had, probably wouldn't be receiving

6
Suggested answers:
1 If she were/was a (more) ambitious person, she would
  have applied for the job of director.
2 If I hadn't met my (German) wife, I wouldn't be living in
  Germany now.
3 If I were/was a risk-taker, I would invest my own money
  in the business.
4 If she had received more encouragement, she would have
  become a pilot *or* she wouldn't have given up her plan of
  becoming a pilot.
5 If I were/was worried about the situation, I would have
  said something about it.
6 If he hadn't left college and become a ski instructor,
  perhaps he wouldn't be so happy with his life.

7
1 C   2 W-W-C   3 C-C   4 W-C   5 W-C

8
1 make   2 do   3 did

9
1 make, do
2 doing, made
3 made, do
4 doing, make

8b (pages 62 and 63)

1
b

2
1 N   2 T   3 T   4 N   5 T   6 N   7 T   8 F

3
1 legacy   2 passing (her) by   3 excuse   4 alternative
5 unlikely   6 support

4
1 would stop   2 could   3 had travelled   4 were
5 hadn't   6 would change   7 hadn't started   8 didn't have

5
1 'd left (= had left)
2 'd stop (= would stop)
3 had
4 were *or* was
5 would take
6 would turn

6
1 match   2 ship   3 chew   4 Swiss   5 shock   6 bass

7
I am very suspicious of bucket lists now. They started out as a good idea, but like a lot of things they have become too commercial. In bookshops you now find titles like *100 Places You Must Visit Before You Die* or *100 Films You Should See*. And if your dream is to hold a baby tiger, there are even websites you can go on where they can make your wish come true.

8c (page 64)

1
1 forest, Cancún, no   2 giraffe, yes   3 tree, Britain, yes

2
1 F   2 T   3 T   4 N   5 N   6 F

3
1 rotting   2 classic   3 sale   4 victims   5 heroic
6 wonderful   7 small   8 rarest

4
1 classic   2 a victim   3 buried   4 for sale   5 rotting

5
Emotive words: back-breaking, desperate, majestic

6
1 rescue   2 deprived   3 giant   4 exploit   5 wonderful
6 most threatened   7 over-developed

8d (page 65)

1
1 d   2 a   3 f   4 b   5 e   6 c

2
They mention: b, d, e

3
1 rather not do   2 'd prefer to do   3 mind helping
4 someone else did   5 'd probably be better   6 like doing

4
1 'd prefer not to do
2 'd rather do
3 be happy to help
4 'd be better
5 'd rather go
6 prefer doing

5
1 Would you prefer   2 Shall we take
3 Would you rather we went   4 Do you like

8e (page 66)

1
1 Speaking loudly on mobile phones is anti-social.
2 No, he doesn't agree. He says speaking loudly is social, not anti-social. It encourages people to be more open with each other.

2a
1 a call to someone to get up, a reminder to buy something from the shops, asking someone to get out of the bathroom
2 when people speak loudly on their mobile phones just to show off

2b
Example answers:
1 shops *or* restaurants
2 shops *or* restaurants
3 the train *or* the underground
4 what they are doing *or* where they are *or* how long they are going to be *or* what they're going to eat for dinner
5 what they are doing *or* where they are *or* how long they are going to be *or* what they're going to eat for dinner

3
a (ought to know better)

4
1 be better   2 go one better   3 know better   4 be better off

Wordbuilding / Learning skills / Check! (page 67)

1
1 plumber   2 florist   3 translator   4 banker   5 pharmacist
6 librarian   7 accountant   8 specialist   9 surgeon
10 consultant   11 inspector   12 optician

2
1 a salesperson   2 a police officer   3 a fire fighter
4 an actor   5 a flight attendant

4
1 Globalization <u>helps</u> <u>people</u> <u>in</u> <u>rich</u> <u>countries</u>.
2 They can have goods out <u>of</u> <u>season</u>.
3 But to be <u>honest,</u> I don't <u>need</u> <u>flowers</u> imported from <u>Africa</u> in <u>December</u>.

6
Across: 2 rocket   5 lemur   6 girl   7 been   9 to   10 if only
11 invisible
Down: 1 goal   3 target   4 ambition   8 noise

Unit 9

9a (pages 68 and 69)

1
Across: 2 criticise   5 urge   6 begs   7 ask   8 deny
Down: 1 accuse   2 complain   3 threaten   4 suggest

2
1 cover, 1982
2 photo, magazine *or* Magazine

3
1 F   2 T   3 F   4 T   5 F   6 F   7 T   8 F

5
1 of manipulating reality.
2 altering the image *or* that they had altered the image.
3 doing anything wrong. *or* that they had done anything wrong.
4 modern technology for making it easy to alter images.
5 their designers (that it is OK) to alter images for covers.
6 about being given a false impression. *or* that they had been given a false impression.
7 not to trust a photo if there's anything important depending on it.

6
1 for invading   2 (for) taking   3 for manipulating
4 to alter   5 using   6 to add   7 for making   8 to accept

7
1 recommends using an analogue camera
2 encourages you to look at the preview before you take a photo; keeps you in the moment
3 that with a digital camera you need more time to edit the images after they've been taken
4 you can make them look like the image as you saw it

9b (pages 70 and 71)

1
1 b   2 d   3 a   4 c

2
a 3   b 2   c 3   d 4   e 1   f 1 (or 3)

3
1 donations   2 zimmer frame   3 brainchild   4 brighten up
5 plunged   6 speeding

4
1 it is estimated that rioters (story 1)
2 The café owner was reported to have put (story 2)
3 It is believed that (story 3)
4 He is not thought to have been speeding (story 4)

5
2 is known   5 was thought
3 used to be believed   6 was said
4 has been estimated

6
2 was hoped that
3 used to be thought that
4 isn't recommended
5 is expected that, will carry on
6 was said to have prevented
7 was considered to be *or* was considered to have been
8 has been reported that

7
1 charming
2 amusing
3 inspiring
4 engaging
5 astonishing
6 optimistic

8
a optimistic
b amusing
c astonishing
d engaging, charming
e inspiring

9c (page 72)

1
b

2
1 a particular   2 two experts   3 man-made   4 both views
5 working for tobacco companies   6 amount of real evidence

3
1 biased   2 fundamental   3 overwhelming
4 distorts   5 proportionate

4
1 b   2 b   3 a   4 a

5
1 word of mouth
2 eat my words
3 one person's word against another's
4 don't take my word for it
5 gave his word
6 From the word go
7 was lost for words
8 have the last word

9d (page 73)

1
1 take (D)   2 gets (B)   3 believe (B)   4 exaggerate (D)
5 surprise (B)   6 take (D)

2
1 He was seen/spotted by a theatrical agent and they want to work with him / sign him up.
2 Kate
3 Not to tell anyone. Patrick wants to keep quiet about it.

3
1 about   2 apparently   3 reckons   4 pinch
5 to   6 heard   7 gossip   8 seems, supposedly

4
1 comedy   2 festival   3 apparently   4 reckon   5 according
6 difficult   7 agency   8 theatrical

5
Students' own answers.

9e (page 74)

1
The correct order is: C, A, D, B

2
1 C   2 A   3 D   4 B

3
1 Whatever the reason
2 The problem is that
3 What is more
4 It is hoped that
5 But now
6 at the same time

4
1 One resident described his life in Bama. 'I have everything I want here,' he said. 'I can go fishing when I want to. I don't have any stress.' And then he added, 'Why would I want to go and live in the city?'
2 'Some people come here to take wedding photos,' said another resident, 'which is fine. But when they leave their rubbish behind, I get very angry.'
3 A health tourist said, 'Before I came here I could hardly breathe or speak, because the pollution in my city was so bad. Now I sing every day,' he said with a big smile on his face.

Wordbuilding / Learning skills / Check! (page 75)

1
1 worrying   2 confusing   3 refreshing   4 charming
5 inspiring *or* touching   6 depressing   7 touching *or* inspiring   8 tiring

2
1 inventive   2 persuasive   3 creative   4 competitive
5 productive   6 talkative   7 protective   8 attractive

3, 4 and 5
Students' own answers.

6
1
Possible verbs:
a agree, offer, refuse, swear
b advise, beg, convince, invite, persuade, recommend, urge, warn
c accuse (... of), blame (... for), congratulate (... on), praise (... for)
2
a iconic   b ageing   c zero
3
a mouth   b good   c gossip   d headline(s)

Unit 10

10a (pages 76 and 77)

1
1 small village in Illinois
2 radio broadcaster; (an) actor (in films and television)
3 the Soviet Union
4 read the lines/words he was given by his advisors
5 listen to people *or* make people feel special
6 (great) economic growth

2
1 b   2 a   3 a   4 b   5 b   6 a

3
1 graduated   2 worked   3 follow *or* pursue   4 joining
5 did   6 become

4
Countries: the United Arab Emirates, the Netherlands
Places: the Amazon River, the countryside, the Moon
Times: the weekend, (the) spring
Others: the police, the poor
All the other nouns take zero article.

5
1 the   2 the   3 the, the   4 a   5 the   6 –, the
7 –, –   8 –, –, –   9 the, the   10 –

6
1 /r/   2 /j/   3 /w/   4 /j/   5 /r/   6 /r/   7 /j/
8 /w/   9 /w/

7
1 I guess I was lucky to do a subject that not many other people at college did. I studied plant sciences and after my course, I got a job as a research assistant at the Institute of Botany.
2 It's not easy to be an artist and make a living from it. You are always wondering if it would be better just to get a job with a regular income.
3 I was always told that having good qualifications and the right degree opens doors, but actually it's good communication skills that help you advance in an organization.

8
1 background   2 experience   3 qualifications
4 qualities   5 knowledge   6 talents

10b (pages 78 and 79)

1
1 My mission is to find simple, inexpensive ways to monitor health
2 these medicines can cause liver damage
3 The small piece of paper is a low-tech tool
4 to attend university
5 I want all women to believe in themselves and know they can transform society *or* to encourage young women who attend university abroad to bring their skills back to their homelands

2
1 c   2 b   3 c   4 a   5 b   6 b

3
1 a   2 b   3 c   4 b   5 c   6 c

4
1 ... could be a medical breakthrough **that will save millions of lives**.
... millions are dying from the same drugs **that are supposed to cure them**.
2 ... is a low-tech tool **which detects disease by analysing bodily fluids**.
3 ... does not surprise people **who know her**.
4 A new foundation **she has launched** ...
5 Positive results, **which show up in less than a minute**, ...
6 she prepared for her college entrance exams, **for which she studied for up to twenty hours a day**.
7 no one monitors patients to see **what** is working and **what** isn't.

5
1 where *or* in which   2 which   3 who
4 what   5 that *or* who *or* no pronoun   6 that *or* which *or* no pronoun   7 with whom   8 whose

6
1 The piece of paper, **which** is the size of a postage stamp, could save thousands of lives. *or* The piece of paper, **which** could save thousands of lives, is the size of a postage stamp.
2 The charity 'Diagnostics for All', **which** was co-founded by Sindi, produces the tool. *or* The charity 'Diagnostics for All', **which** produces the tool, was co-founded by Sindi.
3 The tool will be used in developing countries **where** it is difficult to find clinics.
4 People say things about existing drugs, which I agree with. *or* People say things about existing drugs, with which I agree. *or* I agree with the things (that) people say about existing drugs.
5 The results show up on the paper, **whose** colour changes if there is a problem.
6 Sindi went to England **when** she was a young woman.
7 Sindi, **who** was the first Saudi woman to study biotechnology at Cambridge University, later went to Harvard. *or* Sindi, **who** later went to Harvard, was the first Saudi woman to study biotechnology at Cambridge University.
8 Sindi has become an inspiration for other women **who** want to follow her example.

7
1 She believes that new technology **which was created** at Harvard University will make it possible. *or* She believes that new technology **which has been created** at Harvard University will make it possible.
2 The first thing I ask the children **who are attending** the class is to draw a picture of a scientist.

8
1 suffering   2 living   3 designed   4 determined
5 wishing   6 launched, wanting

10c (page 80)

1
Things to tick: an anti-slavery campaigner, a spy, a nurse, an army officer, a mother, a writer, a public speaker

2
1 b   2 b   3 c   4 a   5 b   6 c

3
1 next door *or* bordering
2 a wonderful place

3 strong-willed, wanting to succeed in something very much
4 the money you get (from a company or the state) when you retire
5 the right for women to have a say in who is elected for public office

4a

1 ef**fec**tive oOo
2 im**pres**sive oOo
3 sup**por**tive oOo
4 **pos**itive Ooo
5 per**sua**sive oOo
6 **sen**sitive Ooo
7 de**ci**sive oOo
8 **tal**kative Ooo

4b
Rule for words that end with vowel + -*tive*: 1st (or antepenultimate) syllable is stressed. For other words, the 2nd (penultimate) syllable is stressed.

5
1 conscious
2 control
3 interest
4 made
5 help
6 confident

10d (page 81)

1
1 in   2 with   3 at   4 of   5 to   6 with   7 on   8 about

2
A job to lead outdoor activities and expeditions for young people.

3
1
Applicant 1: very good with children
Applicant 2: canoeing, water sports and outdoor activities; good organizational skills
Applicant 3: good at a number of different sports; experienced PE teacher

2
Applicant 1: hasn't got experience working with this age group
Applicant 2: hasn't got experience of mountaineering
Applicant 3: hasn't got experience of leading expeditions

4
1 participating   2 to leave   3 travelling   4 doing
5 to work *or* on working   6 to find out *or* in finding out

6
Students' own answers.

10e (page 82)

1
a 4   b 1   c 2   d 3

2
1 which has
2 with an interest in
3 with an ambition to work
4 who has a passion for
5 who has specialist knowledge of
6 with experience in
7 with limited access
8 who loves teaching

3
1 c   2 f   3 e   4 b   5 a   6 d

4
Possible answers:
1 enthusiastic, creative, flexible, adaptable, etc.
2 with
3 specializes

4 aim, goal, ambition, passion, interest
5 which *or* that
6 can
7 have

Wordbuilding / Learning skills / Check! (page 83)

1
The verbs which do not collocate are:
1 do   2 make   3 get   4 make   5 acquire   6 win   7 own
8 work   9 earn   10 take on

2
1 took   2 follow   3 get *or* do   4 had   5 get *or* gain
6 joined *or* set up   7 got *or* gained   8 acquire *or* learn

3
1 d   2 f   3 h   4 b   5 e   6 a   7 c   8 g

4
1 felt   2 definite article   3 acquire *or* get   4 yes
5 semi-formal

5
1 a a mahout   b Daniel Kish *or* the 'real-life' Batman
2 step, mankind
3 a the Atlantic Ocean   d the USA   e the Moon
4 a which is also used (= a defining relative clause)
   b where it is often key (= a non-defining relative clause)

Unit 11

11a (pages 84 and 85)

1
c

2
1 b   2 c   3 c   4 a   5 c   6 a

3
1 aim   2 extinct   3 record   4 diversity   5 centuries
6 express   7 huge   8 understand

4
1 succeeded in discovering
2 were able to help
3 managed to build
4 was able to help
5 could bring
6 couldn't save

5
Possible answers:
1 managed to find *or* was able to find *or* succeeded in finding
2 could speak *or* was able to speak
3 didn't manage to convince *or* didn't succeed in convincing *or* weren't able to convince
4 couldn't understand *or* wasn't able to understand
5 could express *or* was able to express
6 managed to get *or* succeeded in getting; could only remember *or* was only able to remember

6
1 take   2 acquire   3 unaware   4 engage   5 get   6 inspire

7
1 picked up
2 inspire *or* motivate *or* engage with *or* connect with
3 unaware of
4 get *or* understand
5 get *or* understand
6 take in *or* understand

8a
1a Munichi   b Wappo
2a Swarthmore   b Pennsylvania

3 a Arunchal   b Koro
4 chary
5 floccinaucinihilipilification

8b
a 5   b 2a   c 4   d 1b   e 3b

11b (pages 86 and 87)

1
a 2   b 1   c 3

2
1 T   2 F   3 F   4 N   5 F   6 F   7 F   8 T   9 T

3
1 block (something) out   2 ran into   3 came up (to)
4 turned out (that)   5 come across   6 get away with

4
Text 1
1 My sister and I **were just about to go** to bed … *or* **were just going to go** to bed …
2 My sister **was going to say** goodnight … *or* **was about to say** goodnight … *or* **would have said** goodnight.

Text 2
3 I **would have asked** his name … *or* **was going to ask** his name
4 I **was supposed to know** …

Text 3
5 who **was going to give** evidence in court … *or* **was supposed to give** evidence in court … *or* **was about to give evidence** in court …
6 her neighbour **wasn't going to get away with** it …

5
1 was going to write *or* would have written
2 was just about to book, would be full
3 would speak
4 would have lasted *or* was supposed to last, were about to finish *or* were going to finish
5 was going to take *or* would have taken *or* was supposed to take
6 was just about to ask *or* was just going to ask

6a
1 I was <u>going</u> to <u>email</u> him, but I decided it would better to speak face to face.
2 He was <u>supposed</u> to get here <u>early</u>, but he's already ten minutes late.
3 I <u>would</u> have come by <u>train</u>, but there's a strike on at the moment.
4 She said she would be <u>pleased</u> if I talked to him, but she seemed really angry.
5 I was <u>about</u> to <u>buy</u> a flat, but Katie said I could rent hers for six months while she was away.
6 Liz was <u>going</u> to be in charge of the project, but now she's just acting as an advisor.

6b
1 I was going to email him, but I decided it would better to speak <u>face to face.</u>
2 He was supposed to get here early, but he's already <u>ten minutes late.</u>
3 I would have come by train, but there's a <u>strike</u> on at the moment.
4 She said she would be pleased if I talked to him, but she seemed <u>really angry</u>.
5 I was about to buy a flat, but Katie said I could <u>rent hers</u> for six months while she was away.
6 Liz was going to be in charge of the project, but now she's just acting as an <u>advisor</u>.

7
1 c   2 d   3 a   4 e   5 b

11c (page 88)

1
1 border collie   2 crow   3 dolphin   4 Bonobo monkey
5 scrub-jay

2
a 3   b 4   c 1   d 5   e 2

3
a 2   b 3   c 5   d 1   e 4

4
1 smart   2 inventive   3 playful   4 expressive
5 mischievous

5
1 walk   2 late   3 mistakes   4 tricks   5 lesson   6 live
7 way   8 heart

11d (page 89)

1
1 mean   2 speak   3 explain   4 'm   5 saying   6 give
7 take   8 catch *or* hear

2
1 Greek and Roman history
2 He doesn't have as much background knowledge as the other students.
3 Reading some history *or* a book by Herodotus.

3
1 what the course is going to be about
2 no previous knowledge of ancient history is needed
3 stories like the war at Troy and so on
4 a book I could read now, outside class
5 Herodotus

4
1 me   5 me   6 me
The other sentences don't need an indirect personal object.

6
Students' own answers.

11e (page 90)

1
1 c   2 e   3 d   4 b   5 a
The writer's application for a course has been rejected even though he/she applied before the deadline.

2
1 While we sympathize with your situation, it is too late to do anything about it now.
2 Although you sent your form in before the deadline, we had already received too many applications.
3 You say in your letter that we have no right to do this, but in actual fact, the college has the right to close the application process early.
4 We don't 'make up the rules as we go along' as you suggest. On the contrary, we are very careful to follow the rules.
5 Whereas most colleges would keep your application fee, we are refunding it to you.

3
Model answer:

Dear Sir/Madam

I am writing to inform you that I will be unable to attend the accountancy course (B102) this term owing to a misunderstanding.

When I enrolled for the course, I had assumed it was an evening class. In actual fact it turns out to be on Tuesdays between 10 a.m. and 12.30 p.m. I have asked my employer if it would be possible to release me for this period each

Tuesday. Although they would like to do this, they say that the timing makes it impossible.

While I realize that this is probably my fault for not reading the timetable carefully enough, I hope you will be sympathetic. I hope to enrol on a future course, but for the moment I would be grateful if you could refund the course fees I have paid.

I look forward to hearing from you.

Yours faithfully

Mark Riley

Wordbuilding / Learning skills / Check! (page 91)

1
1 point   2 company   3 tip   4 spare   5 room
6 value

2
1 b   2 a   3 b   4 b   5 a   6 a

3, 4, 5 and 6
Students' own answers.

7
1 succeeded   2 engage   3 managed   4 late   5 experience
6 reality
Character 1: SEMLER
7 catch   8 clever   9 heart   10 explain
Character 2: ALEX

Unit 12

12a (pages 92 and 93)

1
1 savers and spenders
2 No, these characteristics are too simplistic.

2
1 b   2 a   3 c   4 a   5 b   6 c

3
fund (v) – finance (v)
prudent – careful
transaction – deal (n)
wages – salaries
wasteful – extravagant

4
1 cost *or* standard   2 haves, nots   3 income
4 standard *or* cost   5 power   6 quality

S	H	A	V	E	S	B
Q	U	A	L	I	T	Y
U	N	I	T	C	A	P
N	G	I	H	O	N	A
O	R	N	E	S	D	S
T	Y	C	Y	T	A	T
S	P	O	W	E	R	E
N	O	M	I	N	D	N
Y	D	E	L	I	V	E

5
1 Let's **just** consider just people's attitude to money at its simplest level.
2 Of course, savers spend only money, but **only** when they can afford it.
3 People in these countries even would have to work longer hours, pay more taxes and **even** accept lower wages.

4 You only don't **only** risk losing the money, but you also risk putting the borrower in a difficult situation.
5 We need both types of person, but **only** if they lend and borrow only responsibly.

6
1 Some people believe that if you go through life ONLY saving money, you will never have any fun. *or* Some people believe that if you ONLY go through life saving money, you will never have any fun.
2 Some people carry on spending money EVEN when they can't afford to.
3 You can protect yourself against bad times by putting aside JUST a small amount of money each week.
4 If ONLY a few people save money, the banks won't have any money to lend to others.
5 It's not JUST me who has debts; other people have them too.
6 Some people say that your attitude to money is JUST to do with your upbringing. *or* Some people JUST say that your attitude to money is to do with your upbringing.
7 Most people are ONLY careful with money when times are hard.
8 Some borrowers admit that sometimes EVEN they borrow money irresponsibly. *or* EVEN some borrowers admit that sometimes they borrow money irresponsibly.

7
1 payments   2 spending   3 investment   4 loan   5 savings
6 borrowing   7 debts   8 earnings

8
I think that people often get into debt because they want a lifestyle that they can't really afford.

It's a lifestyle which is sold to them constantly through advertisements, for example on TV and in magazines.

This desire to have a better lifestyle can affect some governments too. They want to improve their citizens' standard of living so that people will vote for them again.

12b (pages 94 and 95)

1
a

2
1 NG   2 T   3 F   4 NG   5 T   6 T   7 T   8 NG

3
1 dominant   2 mass production   3 profitable   4 wages
5 consumed   6 call centres   7 outsourcing   8 harm

4
1 have people work
2 get their work done
3 have their clothes made
4 get their tuna processed
5 get most questions answered, get them to put
6 get anyone to do, have your own employees do

5a
/ʃ/: machine, revolution
/tʃ/: cheap, richer
/ʒ/: decision, usually
/dʒ/: major, wages

6
1 fit   2 put   3 decorate   4 assemble   5 fixed   6 tiled
7 do   8 cleaned

7
1 b   2 f   3 a   4 d   5 c   6 e

12c (page 96)

1
b

2
1 c   2 b   3 b   4 c   5 a

3
1 passing   2 buzz   3 trend   4 catchy   5 loyal
6 upmarket

4
1a is running hard
1b is hardly running
2a hardly works *or* is hardly
   working
2b works hard *or* is working hard
3 hardly know
4a thought hard
4b hardly thought
5a hardly tried
5b tried hard

12d (page 97)

1
1 h   2 a   3 e   4 b   5 d   6 f   7 c   8 g

2
1 a leaving party for a colleague
2 a reduction in the price

3
1 honest   2 mind   3 hoping   4 would   5 face   6 shoes
7 appreciate   8 key

4
1 L   2 L   3 S   4 L   5 L   6 L   7 L   8 S

5
1 I'm afraid that would be difficult for me.
2 Would you move a bit on the price?
3 Would you be willing to negotiate?
4 I would need to have some kind of guarantee.
5 When would you need to know?
6 I wouldn't want to put you to any trouble.

6
Students' own answers.

12e (page 98)

1
1 As requested   2 Overall   3 specifically   4 Consequently
5 Initially   6 To sum up

2
1 b   2 c   3 a   4 a   5 e   6 c   7 d

3
Possible answers:
1 here is my feedback *or* here are my comments
2 was an excellent course *or* was a very good/useful course
3 some small and large company websites
4 it is very important to know what kind of design is
   suitable for different purposes *or* it was very useful to do
   this comparison
5 to use them, even for someone with no previous
   experience of design
6 would recommend this course
7 time to practise and a bit more guidance with my own
   work

Wordbuilding / Learning skills / Check! (page 99)

1
1 the rich   2 the unemployed   3 the poor   4 the homeless
5 the elderly   6 the famous   7 the adventurous
8 the hard-working   9 the lazy   10 the sick *or* the ill

2
1 P   2 N   3 N   4 N   5 X   6 P   7 P   8 P   9 N   10 N

3 and 4
Students' own answers.

5
1 rainy   2 income   3 catchy   4 have   5 end   6 saving
Word: RICHES

IELTS Practice test

Listening

1 C outside in the grounds
2 B just the morning or the afternoon would suit me fine
3 A you'd have to sign up like anyone else, and there's a monthly fee
4 A tips on how to put a CV together
5 D a seminar led by one of the big recruitment agencies
6 JAYNES J.A.Y.N.E.S
7 Business Studies M: So which faculty's that? Economics? F: Business Studies actually
8 technical translations But this time, she's doing technical translations
9 construction industry he's going to be talking about openings in the construction industry
10 Geology He's working in the Geology department
11 C provides opportunities to meet the scientists who work at the Observatory
12 B an adult single ticket would cost £6.50 in the summer months and £5.50 at other times of year, whereas a family ticket would cost either £24 or £20.
13 C/D explore the universe using hands-on activities
14 D/C the glass-walled café with outside terrace
15 Botany It wasn't the Astrophysics department that bought it, though, but the Botany department
16 meteor shower installed just in time to observe a meteor shower
17 1947 in 1947, the 218-foot Transit Telescope
18 Mark 1/One/I This was named the Mark One Telescope
19 solar system a scale model of the solar system
20 World Heritage to place Jodrell Bank on the UK shortlist for consideration as a site with World Heritage status
21 A how you balance these two aspects is up to you
22 C I hadn't even chosen a specialty – so that made it tough.
23 B I'd have done better with a straight four-week split.
24 A talk to people ... That's how I found the one I went with
25 emergency I went for emergency
26 beach photos ... of the beach that drew me to Belize
27 300,000 with only 300,000 people
28 (the) north up in the north where I was
29 Cuban a lot of the doctors working there are actually Cuban
30 teaching (the staff) I'd rather think of teaching the staff
31 One/1 metre/meter that grows to around one metre
32 Dark brown the male ... being a dark brown
33 Silver(-)grey/grey the female is distinguishable by its silver-grey skin
34 (Dense) undergrowth has a preference for dense undergrowth
35 Lizard(s) tends to rely on lizards as its main source of food
36 Bird Bird island, the place where one was eventually spotted
37 (six-week) survey They commissioned a six-week survey
38 100 supporting a racer population of around 100 individuals
39 B/C The right kind of habitat is not found over a wide area
40 C/B although the snake's habitat does remain vulnerable to hurricane damage

Reading

1 TRUE start by identifying the appropriate granting body to contact
2 TRUE check ... the deadline for the submission of applications
3 FALSE Your proposal should be written out in the format stipulated
4 FALSE It's a good idea to propose only those objectives that you feel relatively confident of achieving within the grant period
5 NOT GIVEN (there is no mention of whether this is advisable or not)
6 TRUE cover what is already known about the problem in the scientific literature
7 FALSE In addition, many forms now have a section ... required to describe how the research is likely to contribute to economic development
8 NOT GIVEN (there is no mention of whether they do this or not)
9 TRUE state clearly that you're aware of the limitations of your approach
10 FALSE describe briefly any particular strengths of your laboratory
11 iii like to see a concise description of the results of any work you have already carried out
12 v your application should include latitude and longitude, elevation, vegetation ...
13 vii Describe how you plan to find people to take part in experiments
14 ii laboratory procedures ... a brief description of the various analytical techniques that you will carry out
15 vi how it will be entered on a computerised database and what software will be used
16 viii the partners with whom you intend to work
17 C evidence for at least 15 separate occasions when it acted as a home
18 B predate other known instances of plant matting by approximately 50,000 years
19 A a tree whose foliage contains chemicals that kill biting insects. Dr Wadley thus thinks ... mattresses on which the inhabitants slept
20 A a range of hitherto unknown artefacts ... pictograms
21 C a range of hitherto unknown artefacts ... arrows
22 D a range of hitherto unknown artefacts ... needles
23 (a/the) tree(s) They probably settled in trees at night
24 climbing they still retained features useful for climbing, such as curved fingers and long arms
25 chimpanzees just as chimpanzees do today
26 fire once hominids learned how to control fire they discovered they could sleep on the ground
27 grass Neanderthals were also building grass beds
28 YES a group of more than sixty cognitive psychologists and neuroscientists signed a document stating that the brain training industry took advantage of people's anxieties and was not supported by sufficient research.
29 NOT GIVEN (There is no information in the text regarding the attitudes of the participants in the study towards the results.)
30 YES In a 2015 survey of the general public, the majority of respondents believed that memory was a natural element of brain function, but in reality, the brain is programmed to forget information in case it becomes overloaded.
31 NO It recognizes six key types of memory – including remembering words and faces – all of which are equally significant
32 NO The Clinic conducted a study on elderly subjects who all carried the gene for Alzheimer's disease (APO-E4) but were otherwise in good physical health.
33 NOT GIVEN (There is no information in the text regarding the number of subjects in the study.)

34 driving   Driving is another such commonplace skill
that studies show has been enhanced by Merzenich's
techniques.

35 injury   those who have suffered a serious head injury
appear to respond positively.

36 prison   these techniques might be used with offenders
who have been sent to prison

37 medication   conventional medication is ineffective for
treating many of the symptoms she observes

38 motivation   it can be difficult for them to maintain
sufficient motivation

39 nutrition   there are also other factors involved, notably
the role of proper nutrition

40 doctors / Doctors   doctors seldom see the value in her
techniques ... the benefits of brain training could be
experienced much more widely